S320
Science: Level 3

Infectious disease

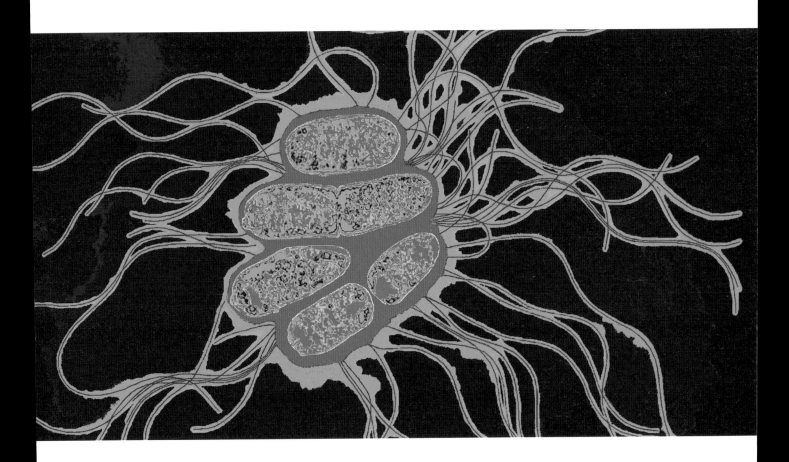

Book 5 Evolving Infections

Prepared for the Course Team by Michael Gillman and Tim Halliday

This publication forms part of an Open University course S320 *Infectious disease*. The complete list of texts which make up this course can be found at the back. Details of this and other Open University courses can be obtained from the Student Registration and Enquiry Service, The Open University, PO Box 197, Milton Keynes MK7 6BJ, United Kingdom: tel. +44 (0)845 300 60 90, email general-enquiries@open.ac.uk

Alternatively, you may visit the Open University website at http://www.open.ac.uk where you can learn more about the wide range of courses and packs offered at all levels by The Open University.

To purchase a selection of Open University course materials visit http://www.ouw.co.uk, or contact Open University Worldwide, Walton Hall, Milton Keynes MK7 6AA, United Kingdom for a brochure. tel. +44 (0)1908 858793; fax +44 (0)1908 858787; email ouw-customer-services@open.ac.uk

The Open University
Walton Hall, Milton Keynes
MK7 6AA

First published 2003. Second edition 2008.

Copyright © 2003, 2008 The Open University

Edited and designed by The Open University.

Typeset by The Open University.

Printed and bound in the United Kingdom by The University Press, Cambridge.

ISBN 978 0 7492 1929 1

2.1

THE S320 COURSE TEAM

Course Team Chair

Michael Gillman

Course Manager

Viki Burnage

Course Team Assistant

Dawn Partner

Course Team Authors

Basiro Davey (Books 1 & 7)

Tim Halliday (Book 5)

Paddy Farrington (Book 6)

Michael Gillman (Books 1 & 5)

Hilary MacQueen (Books 2 & 4)

David Male (Books 1, 3 & 7)

Consultant Authors

Eric Bowers (Book 2)

Christine Heading (Book 7)

Laura Hibberts (Books 2 & 4)

Ralph Muller (Book 7)

Editors

Gerry Bearman

Pat Forster

Gilly Riley

Margaret Swithenby

Academic Reader

Mary Manley

External Course Assessor

Bo Drasar

OU Graphic Design

Roger Courthold

Sian Lewis

Video Editing

Wilf Eynon

Michael Francis

CD-ROM Production

Greg Black

Phil Butcher

BBC Production

Martin Kemp

Rights Executive

Christine Brady

Picture Research

Lydia Eaton

Indexer

Jean Macqueen

Course Websites

Patrina Law

Louise Olney

Sue Dugher

CONTENTS

1 SETTING THE SCENE

1.1 Introduction

This book deals with aspects of the ecology and evolution of hosts and their pathogens, the biology of which has been discussed at length earlier in this course and in OU courses that you may have already studied. As background reading to this chapter, you may find it helpful to read Chapters 1 and 4 from S204 Book 4, available on the *Reference* CD. A total of three study hours has been allocated to this chapter with five hours for Chapter 2, four hours for Chapter 3 and two hours for directed reading. Chapter 1 of Book 1 discussed terminology as it relates to organisms that cause infectious disease. As in the rest of this course, we use the word 'pathogen', but you should be aware that 'parasite' is most widely used in the literature to which this book relates.

The outbreak of bubonic plague known as the Black Death killed more than 25 million people, at least one-third of the population of Europe at the time, between 1347 and 1351; the influenza pandemic that swept the world in 1918 killed twice as many people as the First World War; by the end of 2001, an estimated 65 million people worldwide had been infected with HIV, of whom 25 million had died of AIDS-related illnesses. These are statements about the enormous impact that infectious diseases can have on our species, or on human populations. In this part of the course, we make a fundamental shift in the way that we look at infectious diseases, away from their effect on *individuals*, to their impact on *populations* and *species*. This is the realm of the branch of Biology that is called **Ecology**.

The Black Death and the 1918 flu pandemic were significant events in human history. They were also distinct phases in the evolution of our own species and that of the pathogens which cause these diseases. Humans and the pathogens that affect them evolve together, a process called **coevolution** that we will examine in Chapter 2. In the minds of most people, evolution is about the past; we study the evolution of organisms in order to understand how they have come to be the way they are today. Evolution does not, and has not, stopped; however, humans and their pathogens continue to coevolve. As we will discuss later in this book, important features of human pathogens have changed in recent times and, every year, at least one disease that is new to humans emerges. Moreover, the coevolved relationship is a *dynamic* one, with frequent shifts in the relationship between host and pathogen. Most researchers in the field of human disease believe, for example, that there is a high probability that a major flu pandemic will happen again in the near future.

The application of evolutionary theory and analysis to the biology of infectious diseases has four aspects:

1   The analysis of *process*. All organisms are subject to natural selection which, together with other processes, shapes their genotype and phenotype. It is important that we understand the processes that cause both pathogens and hosts to change over time if we are to combat diseases successfully. The process by which hosts and pathogens coevolve is discussed in Chapter 2.

2   The analysis of *relationships*. As humans, we are concerned with knowing if we are more closely related to gorillas or chimpanzees. It is also important to understand the relationships of our pathogens to pathogens of other species and to non-pathogenic organisms.

3   The analysis of *chronology*. Modern genetic techniques provide a powerful tool that enables us to determine both the relationships between hosts or pathogens and when particular pathogens first evolved. The analysis of relationships and chronology is discussed at various points in Chapter 2 and in Chapter 3, Section 3.5.

4   Shaping the *future*. The efforts of humans to control infectious diseases impose selection pressures on pathogens, causing them to change. Whether such changes will make infectious diseases a lesser or a greater threat to humans in the future depends on our correctly understanding how natural selection works. This is discussed in Chapters 2 and 3 and in the directed reading.

Interest in the evolution and ecology of infectious diseases is comparatively recent. It is only in the last 20 to 30 years that medicine has come to appreciate the central biological notion that 'nothing in biology makes sense except in the light of evolution' (Dobzhansky, 1973). During this time, there has also been a major shift in the thinking of biologists about the role of disease in the ecology of animals and plants, a role that has been previously underestimated. Until recently, ecologists assumed that animal and plant populations are regulated by two processes: predation, and competition for food and other resources. It is now realized that infectious disease is a third major cause of mortality for many species and has, therefore, been a major driving force during their evolution. This observation had been made earlier by Haldane for humans over the last 5000 years (Book 3, Section 5.1).

At this point, it is worth exploring the differences between pathogens and predators, two types of +/− relationship (Box 1.1) both of which include examples of coevolved relationships. Predators are adapted to kill their prey and have evolved many specialized characteristics for doing so. In contrast, it is not generally to the benefit of a pathogen to kill its host because, in so doing, it is likely to bring about its own demise; at best, it creates for itself the very uncertain future of having to find a new host. Pathogens are thus not specifically adapted to kill, as predators are, and, when they kill their hosts, this is best seen as a *consequence* of their activity, not as its objective. Because pathogens rarely benefit from the death of their host, it is commonly argued that pathogens should typically evolve towards being less virulent, that is, towards being commensals rather than pathogens. The evolution of virulence is a major preoccupation of evolutionary biologists interested in disease and, in Chapter 2, we will examine the circumstances in which this argument is or is not supported in the living world.

○   From your general knowledge, do you think that it is realistic to regard predation, competition for food and disease as separate, independent processes?

●   No, this is an unrealistic view. Predators may take as prey those individuals that are weakened by illness or starvation, and it is well known that, for humans, malnutrition may make individuals more susceptible to disease.

This illustrates a major problem facing ecologists studying the impact of infectious diseases on populations of animals or humans: different causes of mortality interact with one another, making it difficult to determine accurately the impact of any one

BOX 1.1   Interactions among species

Six principal kinds of interaction between species are generally recognized: competition, predation, parasitism, commensalism, mutualism and detritivory. These can be categorized according to whether each of the two interacting organisms derives a gain (denoted by a +), incurs a cost (−), or whether there is no impact in fitness terms (0) (see Table 1.1).

TABLE 1.1 A classification of interactions between species.

Interaction	Consequences for species A and B	Comments
competition	0 − or + −	competition in which A competitively excludes B
	− −	competition in which A and B coexist
predation	+ −	includes carnivory, herbivory
parasitism	+ −	A is parasite; B is host
commensalism	+ 0	
detritivory	+ 0	B is dead, so incurs no cost
mutualism	+ +	
neutralism	0 0	

Interactions between animal hosts, such as humans, and microbes fall into three categories. Parasitism is an interaction in which one organism lives in (endoparasite) or on (ectoparasite) another organism, its host, obtaining nourishment at the latter's expense (Book 2, Section 1.1). Typically, the host is not killed by the parasite, but it is harmed to a greater or lesser extent, possibly just by a small blood meal or competition for the host's food. *Where this harm is manifested as a significant amount of damage to host cells, the parasites are referred to as pathogens (disease-causing).* Commensalism (introduced in Book 2) is an interaction in which one organism lives in or on another, its host, at no detriment to the host. Mutualism is an interaction in which two organisms live in a close association, to the benefit of both. Humans have commensal and mutualistic relationships with many microbes, notably the bacteria that live in our guts, some of which may help us digest food.

Parasitism, commensalism and mutualism are all forms of **symbiosis**, defined as the living together in permanent or prolonged association of members (symbionts) of two different species with beneficial or deleterious consequences for at least one of the parties. (Note that some books and papers use symbiosis in the same sense as we have used commensalism and/ or mutualism.)

During the course of evolution, it is theoretically possible for a symbiotic association between a host and a microbe to change from one category to another. The endosymbiotic theory for the origin of complex organisms, for example, proposes that mitochondria are the descendants of microbes that first invaded eukaryotic cells as pathogens or commensals and became mutualists.

of them. A researcher may see a lion kill an impala that the researcher has good reason to believe is already sick or malnourished; is the cause of that death predation or disease?

The hypothesis that, while predation may be the immediate cause of death, disease may have played an important role, has been tested in wild populations of Townsend's vole (*Microtus townsendii*). Experimental animals, treated with an anthelminthic drug, were less likely to be killed by predators than non-treated control voles. It is rare to see obviously sick animals in nature and the reason may often be that predators take them at an early stage of illness. If this is so, it goes some way to explain why ecologists have, until recently, underestimated the importance of infectious disease as a cause of mortality in wild animals.

For humans, we can, fortunately, disregard predation as a significant cause of mortality. We cannot dismiss access to resources, nutrition and public awareness/ education, however. The fact that wealthy western tourists can safari in malaria-infested parts of Africa with virtual impunity, thanks to prophylactic drugs, while thousands of indigenous people die in poverty from malaria is a salutary reminder of the crucial role that the uneven distribution of resources among human populations plays in the ecology of infectious disease. Almost all (95%) of new HIV infections occur in the world's poorer countries.

1.2 The importance of infectious diseases of animals and plants to humans

This course focuses on infectious diseases that affect humans but, in this book, frequent reference will be made to diseases of other animals, and occasionally of plants. There are several reasons for this:

1   Diseases of animals provide valuable data for developing general models of the dynamics of infectious diseases that can be applied to humans. There is no reason to suppose that, apart from the socio-cultural dimensions of disease spread, animal diseases differ in any significant way from human diseases (see (2) below). Much current research on human diseases involves developing mathematical models, such as those advanced by the mathematical biologists Roy Anderson and Robert May, and these are largely based on data from diseases of insects and other animals. (Mathematical models are discussed in Chapter 3 of this book and in Book 6.) It is fair to say that the modelling approach to infectious disease has outstripped the collection of hard data. For example, it was shown, over 20 years ago, that a pathogen could theoretically control the population size of its host, but it has yet to be shown that such a situation occurs in nature. Gathering good data on infectious disease in nature is a very complex and time-consuming task, and those seeking to combat disease are heavily reliant on models. For example, the date of the 2001 General Election in the UK was affected by theoretical predictions as to when the foot-and-mouth outbreak of that year would have run its course.

2   Humans share many diseases with other species (Figure 1.1). A recently developed database of human diseases lists 1415 pathogens that cause disease in humans, of which 61.6% also cause disease in other species. The existence of such a large number of multihost pathogens is very important for combating disease because, as we will see later, the fact that a pathogen occurs in another

species can have a profound effect on its ecology and evolution, and therefore on the way that we seek to control it. For example, the control of rabies has to take account of the fact that the rabies pathogen infects domestic animals, such as dogs, and wild animals, such as foxes.

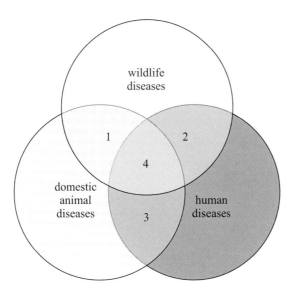

FIGURE 1.1
Overlap among human and animal hosts of infectious diseases. (1) Diseases infecting domestic and wild animals (e.g. canine distemper). (2) Diseases infecting wild animals and humans (e.g. Lyme disease). (3) Diseases infecting humans and domestic animals (e.g. cat scratch fever). (4) Diseases infecting all three (e.g. rabies).

Diseases that can be transmitted from vertebrate animals to humans are called zoonotic diseases or zoonoses (defined in Book 1, Box 1.2). Among diseases that are labelled as 'emerging', that is, that have begun to infect humans in the recent past, 75% are zoonotic. Clearly, other species are an important source of new human diseases. One example is variant Creutzfeldt-Jakob disease (vCJD), which is the human equivalent of bovine spongiform encephalopathy (BSE), or mad cow disease (Book 2, Chapter 4). Another is hantavirus infection, which is caused by a virus transmitted from rodents to humans; humans cannot pass it to one another.

3   Plant and animal diseases can be of enormous economic importance if they affect crops and domestic livestock. Plant diseases destroy about 10% of crops every year worldwide, and the annual bill for fungicides to control plant diseases was estimated in 2001 to be US$6 billion. Moreover, they can have a major impact on food supplies, especially in less-developed countries, and can cause major social disruption.

4   We are living at a time of global ecological difficulties, when biodiversity on Earth is declining rapidly. It is becoming increasingly apparent that infectious disease is often a significant factor in the decline and extinction of plant and animal species. The landscape of Britain and much of mainland Europe was transformed in the 1970s and 1980s by the elimination of elm trees through Dutch elm disease and, at the time of writing (2003), a lethal fungal disease that affects amphibians, called chytridiomycosis (Figure 1.2), is devastating populations of frogs, toads and salamanders throughout the world.

Chytridiomycosis is a tragedy for frogs, and for those people who love them, but is it a cause of concern for humans in general? The answer depends on why frogs and other organisms are being stricken by disease *now*. Disease has undoubtedly

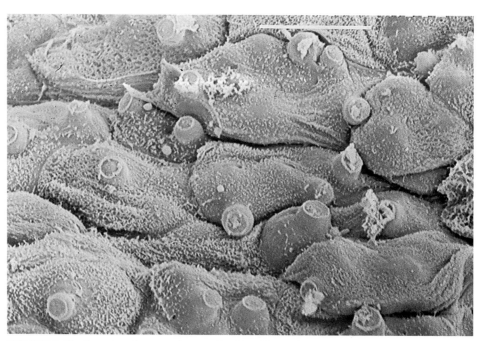

FIGURE 1.2   Scanning electron micrograph of the skin surface from a frog with chytridiomycosis. Fungal discharge tubes are poking through the epithelial surface. (Scale: 10 μm.)

been a fact of life for all but the simplest organisms since the beginning of biological evolution but there is a feeling that major outbreaks, often of apparently new diseases, are becoming more common. There is a problem here, of course; this perception may simply be the result of biologists being much more aware of disease than they were 20 or 30 years ago. It has been suggested, however, that diseases like chytridiomycosis are having a more devastating effect now because the immune system of frogs has been weakened by some other ecological factor, such as pollution, increased UV radiation or climate change. If this hypothesis is correct, then there is a cause for concern among humans, because such factors may be compromising our immune systems too.

Interactions between pathogens and their hosts are complex and, if we are to understand them, we need to get to grips with many aspects of the lives of both protagonists. The following section introduces, explains and defines important terms relating to the life histories and life cycles of host and pathogen. Many of them may be familiar to you, but be prepared to find some terms used in different ways from those you have encountered before.

1.3 Life histories and life cycles

All organisms have a **life history**, which is characteristic for a given species, and which refers to the temporal patterning of four aspects of life: birth, growth, reproduction and death. Some organisms reproduce only once in their lives and are said to be semelparous; organisms that breed several times are iteroparous. The human life history can be summarized as follows: birth followed by growth to about 16 years of age followed by iteroparous reproduction until about age 40 (for females), then post-reproductive life (a feature we share with very few other species) and finally death at around 70 years or much later in many countries from the late twentieth century onwards. In humans, as in most animals, growth slows down or ceases altogether when reproduction begins, a point to which we will return. The study of life histories is primarily concerned with the relative durations and frequency of birth, growth and reproduction and how organisms allocate food and other resources to these activities.

The term 'life history' does not mean quite the same thing as 'life cycle'. The life cycle of a species refers to the particular sequence of phases an individual of that species passes through from birth. Life cycles of several pathogens were described in Book 2 (e.g. Figures 7.1 and 7.19).

There is one other important feature of life cycles that is especially relevant to interactions between hosts and pathogens. This is the movement or transmission of pathogens between hosts. Individuals of many non-pathogenic species make short- or long-distance migrations once or more during their lifetimes. For pathogens, migration between hosts, often occurring at fixed points in the life cycle, is an occupational hazard. The pathogen and its offspring must find new hosts or the population will become extinct. The process of transmission of pathogens between hosts is discussed in detail in all three chapters.

1.3.1 Host life histories and life cycles

Within a host or pathogen species, there is typically much variation in all life history parameters. We know this from our own experience of humans; some individuals reach sexual maturity earlier than others, some live longer than others, etc. Some of this variation is environmental; for example, in developed countries, improved nutrition has lead to earlier sexual maturity. There is also a genetic component to life history variation, which is of great evolutionary significance, as we will see later.

Natural selection shapes the life history of a species so as to maximize individual **fitness** (see Box 1.2). Since fitness is defined in terms of reproductive success, this statement may appear to suggest that all organisms should go all out for reproduction as early in their lives as possible. This, clearly, is not the case; many animals, including humans, do not start breeding until they are quite old. An important factor here is body size. For many female animals, reproductive success (i.e. the survival and number of her offspring) is related to their body size, so that delaying breeding allows growth to a size that optimizes reproductive success. There is a **trade-off** to be considered here, however. The longer a female delays breeding, the greater is her risk of dying first.

BOX 1.2   Fitness

Fitness is a very important concept in evolutionary biology, but its precise definition and measurement are problematic. In host species, it refers to individuals and is a measure of reproductive success, defined as the number of their genetic descendants. It is a relative measure, the most fit individual in a population being assigned a fitness of 1, and all other individuals a fitness of less than 1; such measurements are made under natural conditions. It is thus a measure of relative success resulting from natural selection. In many studies, the number of genetic descendants is measured as the number of first-generation progeny (children) but, ideally, it should be measured over more than one generation to include grandchildren, great-grandchildren, etc. There are very few studies of wild animals or plants in which fitness has been measured over more than one generation and, in general, biologists have to settle for the number of first-generation progeny, and make the assumption that this is a good estimate of 'true' fitness.

Determining the reproductive success of individual pathogens is clearly extremely difficult and the concept of fitness is applied to pathogens in a quite different way. It usually refers to a specific strain and is measured as the number of new infected hosts that result from infection within a single host.

Trade-offs in the host between defence, survival and reproduction

The concept of a life history trade-off is central to understanding the life history of both hosts and pathogens. An organism acquires resources during its life that it has to allocate, as nutrients and energy, either to growth and survival (called somatic effort) or to reproduction (reproductive effort). In many animals, including humans, resources are allocated entirely to somatic effort until body size is sufficient to allow successful reproduction, at which point resources are allocated to reproduction. As a result, growth in most animals ceases or slows down considerably at the onset of reproduction.

In iteroparous species, there are important trade-offs between current and future reproduction. In human females, for example, giving birth to twins may seem to be adaptive because, potentially, it doubles reproductive success. If resources are scarce, however, both babies may die, whereas a single baby might have survived, or, if one twin dies, the survivor might turn out to be smaller and weaker than a single baby would have been. An additional cost of having twins in a low-resource environment may be that it delays the time at which the mother is able to give birth again. The fact that twinning, which has a genetic basis, is rather rare in humans suggests that, over most of human history, it has been more adaptive to have one baby at a time. In trade-off terms, current reproductive effort is constrained to enhance future reproductive success.

An important component of somatic effort is defence against infectious diseases. If they are to survive to breed, host animals must allocate resources to maintaining an immune system as well as to growth, survival and reproduction. Here evolutionary biologists and ecologists face a problem, as it is not at all clear how much it costs, in comparison to growth and reproduction, to maintain an effective immune system. Generally, it is assumed that the resource costs are high, but this is not based on direct measurements and there are some biologists who question the assumption that maintaining an effective immune system is costly.

Table 1.2 presents the results of some animal studies that appear to support the hypothesis that the costs of maintaining immune defences are high, and that they are traded off against reproductive effort.

☐ What other interpretation might be placed on the evidence that red grouse females treated with the drug that eliminates helminth parasites rear more young?

TABLE 1.2 Evidence for a trade-off between reproductive effort and immunocompetence.

Species	Evidence	Interpretation
great tit (*Parus major*)	parents with experimentally enlarged broods have higher pathogen loads	increased reproductive effort leads to reduced immunocompetence
bighorn sheep (*Ovis canadensis*)	lactating ewes have higher pathogen loads than non-lactating ewes	lactation diverts resources from the mother's immune system
	ewes rearing sons (which are larger) have higher pathogen loads than ewes rearing daughters	sons require more resources than daughters
red grouse (*Lagopus lagopus*)	females treated with a drug that eliminates helminth parasites rear more young	reducing the need to mount an immune response releases resources for reproduction

It may be nothing to do with the immune system. It could be that the parasites compete for host resources or have some other effect that indirectly affects reproduction. It may also be that the drug has an effect on the reproductive system.

While results such as these are highly suggestive, they are not conclusive. Reproduction involves sex hormones that, as we will see below, have direct effects on the immune system. As a result, changes in immunocompetence during reproduction may not simply be due to animals redirecting resources from immune defence to reproduction.

Anyone who follows sport is likely to be puzzled by the frequency with which prominent athletes fall ill. After all, exercise is generally assumed to make a person healthier. Highly trained athletes do show a higher than normal incidence of mild to severe illness. One explanation for this is that very high levels of training involve a trade-off, with resources being diverted from the immune system. It is more likely, however, that the effect is hormonal. Athletes are often also under severe stress to win and stress induces elevated levels of hormones such as cortisol which affect the immune system. The causal basis of these effects is not important to us here; what is important is that high investment, either in reproduction or in physical exercise, may incur a cost in terms of reduced immunocompetence.

Age-specific susceptibility to infection

An aspect of host life history that is particularly relevant in the context of infectious disease is age-specific susceptibility to infection. In humans, children and the elderly are at higher risk of contracting infectious diseases, but for very different reasons. Babies may be protected against many diseases by antibodies transferred from the mother via the placenta prior to birth, but this passive protection falls rapidly (Figure 1.3). As infants are exposed to pathogens, they develop their own antibodies but, until these have built up to adult levels, children are more susceptible to infections than adults.

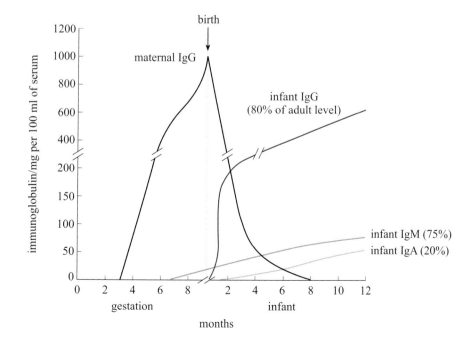

FIGURE 1.3
Levels of antibodies in the circulation of the human fetus in the first year after birth. The figures in brackets after each immunoglobulin class are the percentage of adult levels of that antibody in infants at one year of age.

15

Allele

one pair of genes that occupy the same relative positions on homologous chromosomes and produce different effects on the same process of development.

In birds, mothers similarly protect newly hatched chicks by depositing immunoglobulin Y (IgY), which is the avian equivalent of IgG in egg yolk. They also deposit carotenoid pigment, which makes egg yolk yellow, orange or red; this protects IgY from the harmful effects of free radicals.

In elderly people, reduced immunocompetence is but one of many aspects of deteriorating function associated with ageing and is called senescence. As a result, diseases like influenza and pneumonia are more frequent and/or more severe among the elderly. There is considerable debate about the evolution of ageing that essentially addresses the question: why has natural selection not produced organisms that do not age? The simple answer is that it cannot. Many genes are age-specific in their action, an obvious example being those controlling morphological and other changes at adolescence. Alleles that cause any kind of deterioration before an organism has reproduced will tend to be eliminated by natural selection, because individuals carrying them will have reduced reproductive success. Alleles that cause deterioration later in life, however, cannot be eliminated because they have already been passed on. Thus a major cause of senescence, including the reduced effectiveness of the immune system, is the cumulative effect of late-acting alleles.

Pity the poor male?

A common finding from the analysis of animal life histories is that males suffer higher mortality and, consequently, have lower average longevity than females. There are very few species in which mortality is higher in females. This effect is seen in humans and is attributable to several factors (Figure 1.4). Males lead more hazardous lives than females and are more likely to be murdered or die through accidents, effects that become apparent at puberty. In addition, from the age of about 25, men are more likely to die as a consequence of infectious disease.

Comparative studies across mammals suggest that this effect is related to **sexual dimorphism** in body size; in the majority of mammals, males are larger than females. Sexual dimorphism is relatively slight in humans but is very large in some mammals; for example, mature elephant seal (*Mirounga angustirostris*) bulls weigh three times as much as females. An analysis covering 355 species of mammals revealed that there is a strong association between male-biased parasitism and the degree of sexual dimorphism in body size. Species in which males are very large carry relatively higher pathogen loads.

Correlational data are highly suggestive, but are not conclusive evidence of a causal relationship. Ideally, experimental data are required. Soay sheep (*Ovis aries*) living on St. Kilda, Scotland have been studied over many years. Soay rams are much larger than ewes, have an average annual mortality rate twice that of ewes, and have significantly higher rates of infection with gastrointestinal nematodes. Experimental removal of these pathogens (using drugs) from yearling males and females eliminated the male-biased mortality, confirming that pathogens are the cause of sex-biased mortality in these sheep.

There are a number of possible explanations for higher pathogen loads in males, none of which mutually excludes any of the others:

(i)   Larger animals present a larger 'target' and so are more likely to be found by pathogens.

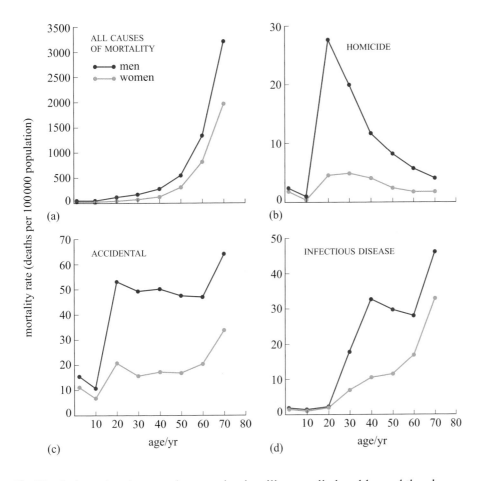

FIGURE 1.4
Sex differences in human mortality.
(a) Mortality rate in males is higher than in females from puberty onwards.
(b) Mortality due to homicide.
(c) Mortality due to accidents.
(d) Mortality due to infectious disease.
(*Note:* the data do not extend beyond 70 years of age.)

(ii) Size being related to age, larger animals will generally be older and thus have had more opportunity to be infected by pathogens.

(In relation to (i) and (ii), there is a positive correlation, across species, whereby larger and longer-lived species are host to a greater number of pathogen species.)

(iii) Males engage more in activities that expose them to pathogen infection, such as fighting.

(iv) For a male to grow large, he has to direct resources away from other functions, including immune defence. In other words, there is a trade-off between immune defence and growth.

(v) Increased male body size at sexual maturity is, in part, a response to increased testosterone levels. Testosterone has a suppressive effect on the immune system.

Whatever the reasons, a large number of studies of animals have shown a positive relationship between male reproductive effort and pathogen loads. Males pay a high price, in health terms, for reproductive success. The association between sex and pathogens has a number of interesting ramifications that we will explore in Chapter 2.

1.3.2 Pathogen life histories and life cycles

The life histories of pathogens are very different from those of their hosts. But, as you will be aware from previous books and case studies, there is a bewildering diversity of pathogen life histories. In some cases, longevity may be very short, perhaps less than an hour. In these organisms, e.g. some bacteria, growth may be very rapid. Furthermore, bacteria do not die under normal circumstances unless due to accident or infection by phages – they just divide! In contrast, some individual pathogens may live for months or years in their host. There is also a wide range in the numbers of offspring produced.

Following its entry into a host (infection), the pathogen finds its way to its preferred home within the body. There are two important variables related to this phase of the pathogen's life cycle:

1   The **latent period**. This is the time period from infection until the host begins to release the pathogen's progeny, i.e. until the host becomes infectious (Figure 1.5).

○   What is the distinction between latent period, as described here, and latent infection, as described in Book 1, p. 21?

●   A latent infection is one in which a pathogen may be hidden in the host without causing disease symptoms (we refer to this as the dormant period below, to avoid confusion with the latent period as defined here).

2   The **incubation period**. This is the time period from infection until the host begins to show symptoms.

The latent period is always shorter than the incubation period; in other words, the host can pass on the disease before it has developed symptoms (Figure 1.5).

Another variable that is important to know for preventing the spread of a disease is its **infectious period** (Figure 1.5). This is the time for which, following infection and the latent period, a host can pass on the disease. For measles-infected individuals, it is six to seven days; for HIV/AIDS individuals, it is several years.

Every organism, be it host or pathogen, has a characteristic **generation time**, defined, for a sexually reproducing species such as humans, as the average span of time between the birth of parents and birth of their offspring. For humans, this is around 20 years; for our pathogens, it can be much shorter. Bacteria can vary in fission time from 12 minutes, through 30 minutes for *E. coli* in the gut, to days for the leprosy-causing bacterium (*Mycobacterium leprae*).

○   Recall from Book 2 the characteristic generation time of the smallpox virus (Figure 3.15).

●   At least 6 to 25 hours (DNA replication and morphogenesis, Figure 3.15).

In other pathogens, such as the protoctists or helminths, the life cycle is indirect, i.e. occurring in more than one host or host and vector. In these cases, the generation time has to be measured across all the hosts from one stage to the completion of the same stage in the next generation.

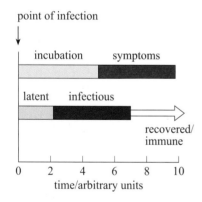

FIGURE 1.5
The relationship between incubation, latent and infectious periods of a pathogen. Note that the infectious period and the duration of symptoms of disease are not necessarily synchronous.

☐ What is the typical generation time of filarial roundworms (Book 2, Figure 7.19)?

⬤ The pathogen spends 10–14 days in the insect vector and anywhere from 3 to 12 months in the human host. Therefore, generation time may be from 3.5 to 12.5 months.

Finally, whether or not an infection leads to illness may depend on the number of pathogens that enter the body at the time of infection. For hepatitis B, one virion can cause illness; for other diseases, a large number may be required. For example, *E. coli* 0157 requires about 10–500 individuals, *Salmonella* requires anywhere between 100 to 10^7 (dependent on the strain) and for *Giardia*, 10 cysts are required for infection. In discussing this issue, it is important to distinguish between the actual number required for infection versus the higher probability of infection due to high numbers of pathogens.

☐ Recall from the *Cholera* Case Study the typical number of vibrios per host required to cause cholera.

⬤ 10^8, i.e. 100 million.

This variable is called the **infectious dose**, and is sometimes expressed as the **ID_{50}**, which is the number of pathogens required to make 50% of infected hosts ill. ID_{50} values are determined experimentally, by injecting different doses of pathogen into susceptible animals. Knowing the infectious dose of an organism is important in treatment and control, e.g. determining the level of hygiene that is required to prevent its spread. For a disease like winter vomiting, with a low infectious dose of 10 to 100 virions, very high standards of disinfection are required.

Table 1.3 presents data on the range of variation in these life cycle and host response variables that occurs among the pathogens featured in the case studies in this course.

TABLE 1.3 Values for the life cycle and host response variables of the case study pathogens in humans.

Disease	Influenza	Malaria	Cholera	Syphilis	TB	AIDS
pathogen	orthomyxoviruses	*Plasmodium* sp. (protoctist)	*Vibrio cholerae* (bacterium)	*Treponema pallidum* (bacterium)	*Mycobacterium* (bacterium)	HIV
latent period (L)	1+ days	21 days*		up to 4 months		1–2 months
infectious period (I)	3–4 days	1 to 3 years	less than 2 weeks	up to 4 years	months or years[†]	
incubation period	1+ days	12 days to 30 days	usually 2–3 days	9–90 days (average 3 weeks)	4–12 weeks	up to 10 years
duration of symptoms	7–10 days usually	maximum of several years from dormant pathogens in liver cells	about 48 hours	months or years	months or years[†]	several years
infectious dose (no. of organisms)	800	10	10^8	60	not known	uncertain

* See Chapter 3.   [†] Depends on reactivation.

○ Describe the range of variation in the life cycle parameters in Table 1.3.

● In all cases there is enormous variation, especially in the infectious period and duration of symptoms, where the range is from a few days to years – this probably represents up to three orders of magnitude variation (less than 10 to more than 1000 days).

Once established in the host, the pathogen begins to reproduce and it is the host's response to this that usually triggers symptoms. Pathogens vary in the extent to which they spread through the body at this stage. Diseases like influenza usually remain confined to the respiratory tract, but others, like HIV and syphilis, spread to many different parts of the body.

1.3.3 Transmission

We have mentioned the importance of transmission between hosts in the life histories of pathogens. Once outside the host, there are various routes by which pathogens find their way to new hosts. In all of the following discussion, we will consider horizontal routes of transmission.

○ Recall from Book 2, Section 1.5 the routes of transmission.

● The routes listed were via the air, by direct person-to-person contact, by invertebrate vectors, by inanimate objects (fomites) and via food or water.

Examples of these routes of transmission are given in Figure 1.6.

Let us put these routes of transmission into three categories. First, transmission via the abiotic external environment, without involving other organisms, that may be through the air via mucus droplets (colds, influenza), via water bodies or inanimate objects. In these cases, direct contact between hosts is not necessary, although close proximity may increase the likelihood of transmission. Secondly, direct contact between hosts, e.g. diseases that are sexually transmitted (syphilis and other venereal diseases). These pathogens are generally unable to exist outside the host (e.g. *Treponema pallidum*). In contrast, some pathogens transmitted via the abiotic environment can last for months or years outside the host, aided by entering a resistant phase.

○ Recall from Book 2 an example of a pathogen that survives in the soil as an endospore.

● The bacterium that causes anthrax, *Bacillus anthracis*.

In the case of anthrax, transmission time may be decades. The third type of transmission is by an invertebrate vector, several of which you have already encountered in this course, including mosquitoes and ticks. Again, the time spent in the vector may be considerable and, in all cases, is of a minimum duration to allow particular stages of development to occur. For example, *Plasmodium falciparum* needs to spend about 10 days in its mosquito vector in order to complete that stage of its life cycle. This represents an important difference when compared to the transmission modes of diseases via the abiotic environment, where usually no development takes place, and certainly not a different set of developmental stages to that in the host(s). For example, although the endospore of *Bacillus anthracis* is a different developmental stage, the development happens in the vegetative cell (in the

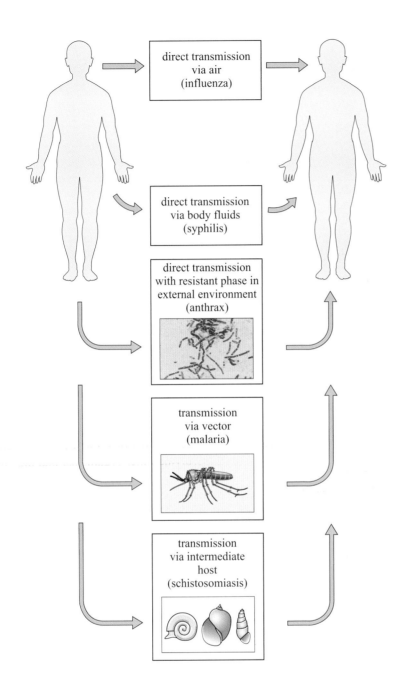

FIGURE 1.6
Examples of routes of disease transmission associated with direct or indirect life cycles.

host) before release into the abiotic environment. However, there are exceptions, for example, hookworms live free in the soil and develop from eggs to infective larva. They then develop into adults in the host (Book 2, Section 7.5.1).

Most tapeworms and flukes spend part of their life cycle in an intermediate host, such as a pig or aquatic snails.

○ Recall from Book 2, Figure 7.1 the methods of transmission between the intermediate and human host.

● The method of transmission is via the abiotic environment, e.g. water or soil. In some cases, movement through the water is aided by swimming towards the next host.

Transmission is a risky process from a pathogen's perspective and, for many diseases, may offer humans the best opportunity to combat a disease. But how can we measure the efficiency of transmission? In Book 6, you will find extensive discussion of aspects of the efficiency of transmission of a pathogen. From both an ecological and epidemiological perspective, we are interested in the number of pathogens transmitted for a given number of pathogens in the infected host. Thus, if an infectious host has 1000 pathogens, what number are able to find a new susceptible host? In other words, what is the probability of successful transfer of pathogens from an infectious to a susceptible host? To determine this, we need to identify two components of transmission.

The first component is the predictability of transmission events. Transmission via the abiotic environment is highly predictable – air, water or soil is usually present around an infectious host. In contrast, transmission by host–host contact is far less certain, although some pathogens increase their chances by exploiting the sexual behaviour of their hosts. Transmission by vectors probably lies somewhere between the two extremes of abiotic and direct contact. Biting mosquitoes are widespread and bite with high and predictable frequency.

The second component is the efficiency with which transmission occurs if the susceptible host encounters the pathogen. Direct contact between hosts offers a highly efficient transmission route for pathogens. The same is true of vectors, especially biting mosquitoes that are able to seek out the peripheral blood supply of the host. In both these cases, the pathogen never has to pass out of the host's or vector's circulatory systems. Transfer via the abiotic environment is far less efficient, because the pathogens disperse within the water body, air or soil. As mentioned above, this is where high densities of the host, such as occurs with TB cases, or use of the same body of water, can dramatically increase efficiency of transmission.

○ Give an example from the *Cholera* Case Study of how use of a particular water supply led to high transmission of the cholera pathogen.

● The study by John Snow in 1854 of the outbreak of cholera around the Broad Street water pump (*Cholera* Case Study, p.6).

Another example was given in Book 2, Figure 7.10, where the prevalence of schistosomiasis was higher for communities living closer to infected rivers. Understanding the routes of transmission and their chances of success are vital in strategies for controlling infectious diseases. Changes in public hygiene have played a major role in control of diseases such as cholera by reducing the effectiveness with which pathogens are transmitted from host to host. In Chapters 2 and 3, we will consider the control of vector-borne diseases by breaking the routes of transmission.

1.3.4 Do pathogens have distinct life-history strategies?

Faced with the enormous range of pathogen life histories (exemplified by the range of values in Table 1.3) and the great variety of routes of transmission, it is tempting

TABLE 1.4 A way of categorizing pathogen life-history strategies.

		Within-host variables		
	minimum duration in host	short (<10 days) § (none)	medium (>10 days) (moderate)	long (>30 days) (complex)
Between-host (transmission) variables	abiotic environment (air, soil, water)	(i) influenza, cholera		TB*
	vector		(ii) malaria	
	host-to-host contact			(iii) syphilis, HIV, TB†

* *Mycobacterium tuberculosis*.

† *Mycobacterium bovis*.

§ level of countermeasure against host defence

rapid reproduction strategy

Stealth + evasion strategy

to conclude that all possible manner of pathogen existence has been exploited and all we can do is simply document that variation. However, ecologists and evolutionary biologists always attempt to seek patterns in the variation (possibly in vain!) and we are no exception on this course. Seeking such patterns is helpful not only in considering how pathogens may evolve and interact with hosts, but also in ordering our thoughts about host–pathogen interactions. We can then discuss these ideas as we progress through the book.

We noted in Table 1.3 that the pathogens appeared to fall into several categories with respect to *within-host* variables, such as incubation period. Similarly, we have also recognized three different categories of transmission that can be referred to as *between-host* variables. If there is some relationship connecting within-host and between-host life-history parameters, then we may be able to recognize distinct life-history strategies. One possible relationship is summarized in Table 1.4.

According to this view, we can place our case-study pathogens, with the partial exception of TB, into one of three categories (i–iii). In the first case (i), exemplified by influenza and cholera, the pathogen reproduces very rapidly in the host and moves on to another host before the infectious host's immune system has had time to develop an effective response.

☐ Recall from Book 1, Figure 2.2, the delay in response of the host immune system to a typical influenza virus infection.

■ Antibodies begin appearing by day 3, which is also the onset of virus particle transmission from the host.

Thus for strategy (i), there is no selection pressure favouring countermeasures against the host defence. Viral particles or bacteria that evade or protect themselves against the host defence are not predicted to have a higher fitness than those that do not have such protection. However, it is predicted that these pathogens need to reproduce rapidly so that large numbers of pathogens can be generated quickly (within 3–4 days) in a single host. Large numbers are required because they are transmitted via the abiotic environment.

At the other extreme is the strategy of stealth and evasion ((iii) in Table 1.4). These pathogens, such as HIV and *Treponema pallidum*, succeed by resisting the immune response of their hosts. In the case of HIV, this is also combined with high rates of production of virions in an infected person. TB is a special case because it can fit into one of two categories, depending on the route of transmission. TB can be transmitted by water droplets through the air or via infected milk (*M. bovis*). In the latter case this is essentially a host-to-host contact, which puts it into category (iii).

☐ Can you recall from the *Tuberculosis* CD some of the complex countermeasures of *Mycobacterium* sp. against the host defence, which help it to persist in the host?

◐ It is able to enter a dormant state in the host, within local foci in the lungs, and in macrophages. Its waxy cell wall helps protect it from the immune response, e.g. by its possession of the glycolipid LAM. This biomolecule confers various protective properties against hosts, including the delay of production of TNF-α in host macrophages, thereby delaying destruction of the macrophage within which the bacterium can persist. (See *Tuberculosis* CD, 'Immunology' CD screen 19 and Book 2, p. 28.)

Mycobacterium tuberculosis also has similarities to *Treponema pallidum* in that it does not persist for long in the abiotic environment, being broken down by UV radiation. This, combined with its dispersal in water droplets, is why transmission is most frequent in dark, humid, overcrowded areas.

Another example of a type (iii) strategy microbe is the virus herpes simplex that causes cold sores. This organism lives for years in its host, being dormant for long periods and only occasionally being infectious. Herpes simplex lives in the nervous system, where it is safe from attack by the host's immune system; the host cannot afford to damage its own nervous system by mounting a full immune reaction.

Some species of *Plasmodium* and *Trypanosoma* can also be long-lived in their host, evading their immune system by repeatedly changing their surface molecules. A detailed account of this is given for *Trypanosoma brucei* in the *Immunology* CD.

In the search for pathogen life-history strategies, we are not just looking for examples of combinations of variables to go into Table 1.4. We are also looking for empty cells in the table that will indicate strategies that are not viable options for pathogens. For example, from Table 1.4 we do not have amongst the case studies an example of a pathogen that has transmission by direct host–host contact but that has a duration in the host of less than 10 days.

☐ Why do you think this may not be a viable option for pathogens?

◐ Because the direct contact between hosts would not be sufficiently frequent for transmission of pathogens. Pathogens in one host would have too low a probability of being transferred to another host, and therefore become extinct.

We will need to test this prediction with other pathogens (starting with Question 1.4 at the end of this chapter).

1.4 Biodiversity

> At the present time, scientific estimates of the number of living species on Earth, including microbes, range from 1.4 million to 200 million. This laughable range means we are simply clueless about the number, let alone types, of living creatures on Earth.
>
> *(All Species Inventory*, 2002)

In view of all the media hype about the advances in Biology over the past 100 years, it is sobering to be reminded of how ignorant we still are about such a fundamental aspect of the subject as the number of species on Earth. In fact, this is just one aspect of the term 'biodiversity' which also relates to the genetic and ecosystem levels of diversity. Modern technologies are helping to elucidate these two levels of diversity. Pertinent to this course, by the end of 2002, molecular biology had provided the genome maps of *Plasmodium falciparum* and one of its vectors, *Anopheles gambiae*. Remote sensing (using satellite systems) analysed via geographic information systems are also helping at the ecosystem level of diversity, e.g. in describing the rate of spread of an infection.

Whilst we do have reasonably accurate figures for some components of biodiversity, our greatest area of ignorance concerns microbes. We know there are about 40 000 vertebrate species, of which about 4600 are mammals and about 8800 are birds. We also know that a high percentage of all described and named species are insects (750 000), of which about 300 000 are beetles. In contrast, it is estimated that the 4000 species of bacteria described to date represent only 0.1% of all bacteria species. More recent estimates suggest this may be a serious underestimate. For example, it was estimated that 30 g of soil, taken from a Norwegian forest, contained 500 000 species of bacteria. Microbial diversity increases towards the equator, thus this value is expected to be much higher in the tropics. The percentages of described 'species' are somewhat higher for viruses (1%), fungi (5%) and protoctists (40%).

There is a serious problem when it comes to estimating the biodiversity of microbes. It is not clear what constitutes a species; indeed, the species concept as applied to multicellular organisms may not be appropriate for microbes.

○ Based on information from Book 2, why may the species concept not be appropriate for microbes?

● Two major reasons for this are: first, that sexual reproduction, which is central to the biological species concept, does not occur in many microbes; and secondly, that very different microbe 'species' can exchange genetic material with one another (see Box 2.2 on mobile genetic elements in Book 2).

How many of these diverse microbes are pathogens? You read earlier that 1415 human pathogens have been described, of which 62% are also symbionts of other species. This means that there are around 540 pathogens that are exclusive to humans. If all 4600 species of mammal have only half that number, there are over one million species of mammalian pathogens in the world that are exclusive to their hosts, and an even larger number that can move between hosts. Human zoonoses do not only come from mammals; a number of diseases, such as West Nile virus, come from birds.

Does any of this matter? Yes, it does, for three main reasons:

1   As mentioned above, around 70% of recently emerged human diseases are zoonotic. This suggests that there may be an extremely large number of pathogens that might find their way into humans in the future.

2   Other species are a major source of drugs to combat disease. Of the top 10 prescription drugs used in the USA until 1995, nine were based on natural plant products. Plant diversity is relatively low in the USA, and other parts of the world, especially the tropics, are likely to be a richer source of new pharmaceuticals. Some frog species secrete compounds in their skin that kill bacteria and viruses, a sensible adaptation for animals living in dirty water. Such sources of compounds that humans might be able to use to combat disease are largely unexplored and there is a serious danger that the loss of biodiversity may eliminate such sources before they have been discovered.

3   The number of pathogenic microbe species is minuscule compared with the overall biodiversity of microbes. The numbers of microbes that live in a human body exceed the number of human cells by at least two orders of magnitude (10^{14} versus 10^{12}). Large numbers of microbes, whatever their environment, leads to intense competition for resources, and microbes are engaged in a constant struggle for existence with one another. One of their adaptations in this struggle is the production of chemical agents that attack, incapacitate or kill other microbes; these are what we call antibiotics. When we attack parasitic microbes with antibiotics, we are using a strategy that microbes have been employing among themselves for millions of years. We should not be surprised, therefore, that microbes can evolve resistance to antibiotics, a topic we return to in Chapter 2, Section 2.6.

Summary of Chapter 1

1   Study of ecology and (co)evolution of infectious disease shifts the emphasis away from individual hosts or pathogens to populations and species.

2   Disease has only recently been widely recognized as an important contributor to mortality in many species, relative to the contributions from predation and competition.

3   Plant and animal diseases are relevant to humans as models of disease, because they have pathogens in common with humans and due to their economic importance and effect on biodiversity.

4   Both pathogens and hosts have characteristic life histories and life cycles which describe, respectively, general and specific features of birth, growth, reproduction, migration (transmission) and death.

5   Hosts may trade-off infectious disease defence (e.g. maintenance of a potentially costly immune system) against growth and/or reproduction.

6   Host organisms of different sex and different stages of their life history may have different levels of susceptibility to infection.

7   Life cycles of pathogens show a wide range of latent, incubation and infectious periods. Other key variables, which may be difficult to measure, are generation time and infectious dose.

8   Pathogen life histories can be categorized according to routes of transmission (between-host characteristics) and duration in hosts (within-host characteristics).

9   Microbial diversity, an important component of biodiversity, is high and poorly established. This, combined with the overlap of human and animal hosts, creates uncertainty for predictions of future patterns of disease.

Learning outcomes for Chapter 1

When you have studied this chapter, you should be able to:

1.1   Define and use, or recognize definitions and applications of, each of the terms printed in **bold** in the text. (*Questions 1.1, 1.3*)

1.2   Give reasons why the study of diseases in plants and non-human animals are important for humans. (*Question 1.2*)

1.3   Show how an understanding of trade-offs between survival, defence and reproduction sheds light on host–pathogen interactions. (*Question 1.5*)

1.4   Give examples of age-specific and sex-specific responses to disease. (*Question 1.5*)

1.5   Describe the main (generalized) stages of the pathogen life cycle and the responses of the host. (*Question 1.3*)

1.6   Categorize the types of transmission and discuss their relationship to within-host variables. (*Question 1.4)*

1.7   Discuss the importance of biodiversity to human–pathogen interactions. (*Question 1.2*)

Questions for Chapter 1

Question 1.1

In this course, we have chosen to use the term pathogen in preference to parasite. Provide a short account of reasons for and against such an argument.

Question 1.2

Give two examples of human diseases that require the study of diseases in other organisms. Provide a brief justification for your choices.

Question 1.3

Summarize the life histories of human hosts and their pathogens. What, if any, are the fundamental differences between the two life histories?

Question 1.4

Where do the following diseases fit into the scheme of Table 1.4? Do they provide support for recognizable pathogen life-history strategies? You may have to refer back to Book 2 for some of the details.

Cryptosporidium, Trypanosoma brucei, filarial roundworms, herpes simplex, schistosomes and transmissible spongiform encephalopathies (TSEs).

Question 1.5

Describe one example of a host life history trade-off involving defence against pathogens that is likely to change with host age.

2 COEVOLUTION OF HOSTS AND PATHOGENS

Tadpoles of the North American green frog (*Rana clamitans*) are parasitized by a trematode (*Echinosterma* sp.), the dispersal phase of which (cercariae) enter via the tadpole's cloacal opening and invade its kidneys. In a sample of 200 tadpoles, 97% had pathogens only in the right kidney. This lateral bias by the pathogen ensures that its tadpole host, which can survive the destruction of one kidney, but not both, does not die, to the benefit of both host and pathogen.

Lizards are often parasitized by ticks and mites, which tend to cluster around the host's eyes and ears and in skin folds, to the irritation of their host. The Spanish lizard *Psammodromus algirus* has a little pocket of skin on each side of its neck that provides an ideal home for the tick *Ixodes ricinus*. Unless the number of ticks on an individual lizard becomes very high, they remain mostly in the pouches, leaving other parts of the host tick-free.

These and numerous other examples illustrate the intimacy that characterizes many coevolved relationships between hosts and their pathogens. As emphasized in Chapter 1, pathogen–host relationships are fundamentally different from predator–prey relationships in that both partners generally have a shared interest in the host's survival. As a result, adaptations have evolved in hosts, which cannot avoid pathogens, that mitigate their adverse effects. For their part, many pathogens have evolved adaptations that reduce the threat they pose to the health and survival of their host. However, the pathogens with which we are concerned in this course make people very sick and often kill them. Why are some pathogens benign and others lethal? In this section, we examine aspects of the life history and ecology of pathogens and hosts that favour the evolution of coexistence and consider whether it is the inevitable evolutionary outcome of all pathogen–host associations.

2.1 What is coevolution?

Coevolution, introduced in Chapter 1 and Book 2, Section 7.6, is a word that is widely used in evolutionary biology, often rather loosely, in the context of intimate relationships between species, such as between plants and the insects that pollinate them. Strictly defined, coevolution refers to relationships in which the evolution of a particular trait in one species has led to the evolution of a particular trait in another. For example, in the context of infectious diseases, the evolution of the ability of a host to detect and respond to an infecting pathogen at an early stage has lead, in many pathogens, to the evolution of adaptations that enable it to evade host defences. In Chapter 3, we will discuss how coevolution has led to increased specialization.

There are three contrasting models of how hosts and pathogens can coevolve:

1   *Mutual Aggression*. Host and pathogen are engaged in an evolutionary 'arms race', with each species continually evolving in an aggressive manner toward the other (this was the example of coevolution given in Book 2, Section 7.6). In the pathogen, selection favours greater exploitation of the host; in the host, selection favours more effective exclusion of the pathogen.

2   ***Prudent Pathogen***. Selection in the pathogen favours traits that limit the harm it does to the host. As a result, the host and pathogen survive longer. From the host's point of view, it can invest fewer resources in defence and so comes to tolerate the pathogen. Note that this model assumes host defences against pathogens are costly, an assumption to which we will return.

3   ***Incipient Mutualism***. Pathogen and host not only evolve towards doing one another less harm, but also evolve ways to benefit one another.

These three models are well illustrated by the many microbes that make up the normal flora that live on and in animals, particularly in the gut. The number of individual microbes that make up the normal flora is enormous. The majority of these microbes appear to have no harmful or directly beneficial effect on their host and so illustrate the Prudent Pathogen model. For some animals, notably ruminant mammals such as cows, certain species of bacteria play a vital role in breaking down specific components of food, such as cellulose, which the host cannot digest itself. Such bacteria are mutualists, and if evolved from pathogens, illustrate the Incipient Mutualism model. Occasionally, the gut may be infected by a harmful microbe, such as *E. coli* 0157 or *Salmonella*, which can kill its host; these exemplify the Mutual Aggression model.

2.2 Variation and reproduction

When a pathogen infects a human population, it is immediately apparent that there is a great deal of variation among individual hosts. Some do not become ill at all, some are only mildly affected, some are very ill indeed and others may die. The causes of this variation are many and varied. Some individuals are just lucky and do not get infected; some receive a larger dose of pathogen than others; some are more susceptible than others to the pathogen. Variation in susceptibility may reflect variation in exposure to the disease earlier in life, it may be due to overload of an individual's immune system as caused by a number of superimposed infections compounded by poor diet, or it may have a genetic basis. In this section, we are primarily concerned with genetic variation, both among hosts and among pathogens; it is the interplay between host and pathogen genotypes that provides the basis of their coevolution.

Genetic variation is the fundamental basis for evolution by natural selection. If there is no genetic variation in a character, it cannot evolve. In this section, we will explore the nature and sources of genetic variation in hosts and pathogens. A major source of variation is reproduction and so we will also consider the nature of reproduction in the two partners in their coevolved relationship.

2.2.1 Variation and reproduction in hosts

The development of new techniques for analysing genomes has made it possible to quantify the genetic basis of variable susceptibility to infectious diseases. For example, 12 genes have been identified that contribute to susceptibility or resistance to malaria in humans. For large, complex organisms such as humans, the major source of genetic variation is sexual reproduction. Many organisms reproduce asexually, either facultatively or obligately, and we will consider the significance of this in relation to infectious disease later. During sexual reproduction, meiosis and syngamy (fusion of gametes from different parents) involve genetic reassortment and recombination, as a result of which offspring have unique genotypes. Other sources of genetic variation are mutation and, at the level of populations, genetic drift.

Genetic mutations occur spontaneously, but mutation rates are accelerated by a variety of environmental factors such as chemical pollutants and increased radiation, e.g. radioactivity and UV-B. Few mutations are expressed phenotypically; many are eliminated by DNA repair mechanisms, others are eliminated by natural selection during development, while others are recessive and not expressed in diploid or polyploid organisms. Nevertheless, in organisms with large genomes, such as humans, every individual carries a small number of novel mutations.

Genetic drift is a factor in small, relatively isolated populations of a species. Such populations contain a random sub-set of all the alleles in the genome of that species. Genetic drift is an important factor in many aspects of host–pathogen coevolution. For example, small, isolated populations of humans and other vertebrate animals are often more susceptible to a particular disease because, by chance, they lack alleles protecting that species against that disease. It may also be important, as we will see later, in the evolution of pathogens.

Contemporary host populations show enormous genetic variation that is the result, not only of mutation, drift and reproduction, but also of natural selection. The genome of a species is the result of generations of natural selection and reflects its evolutionary history. This is very apparent in the context of infectious disease. In humans, a genetic basis for variation in susceptibility to infectious diseases has been revealed by a variety of techniques. The frequency of some susceptibility alleles shows a very strong association with disease. For example, alleles associated with immunity to malaria are much more common in Africa, which has long been exposed to this disease, than in other parts of the world that have no history of exposure to it (see *Immunology* CD2 'Malaria' lecture).

☐ Recall from Book 3 an example of genetic variation related to historical variation in malarial incidence.

⬤ The high frequency of HLA-B35 alleles in lowland areas of Sardinia where malaria was (historically) more frequent (Chapter 5, Section 5.1).

In contrast, alleles that influence the infectivity of HIV, a very recent disease, are expected to be much less common in the human population. In Book 3, we described how the allele called CCR5Δ32 provides low or high protection against AIDS, depending on whether it is in the heterozygous or homozygous state. These alleles are predicted to increase in frequency, because they prolong survival during peak reproductive years. In fact, this allele frequency is about 10% in Caucasians, which is more common than most alleles that affect malaria susceptibility. It is not known why CCR5Δ32 should occur at such a high frequency. The mutation itself does not seem to be deleterious to the immune system, since other linked genes can carry out the functions of this particular chemokine receptor. We can speculate that either (1) it is a duplicate gene that has arisen by chance; until now it has been evolutionarily neutral and has coincidentally been common in the gene pool, or (2) it is linked to a gene which has a definite evolutionary advantage – possibly another chemokine receptor.

The most highly variable part of the genome of humans and other mammals is the major histocompatibility complex (MHC), introduced in Book 3, of which HLA-B35 is one variant. The MHC consists of a small number of linked genetic loci that code for human leucocyte antigens (HLAs). Six loci are commonly recognized, called HLA-A, -B, -C, DP, DQ and DR. These loci are highly polymorphic and an ever-increasing number of alleles are being identified. The number of alleles known by late 2002 was 206 at HLA-A, 403 at HLA-B, 92 at HLA-C and 400+ at HLA-D. Such levels of genetic polymorphism are far greater than anything known for other parts of the human genome. At most loci in the human genome, the number of alleles is in single figures. Different human populations have different MHC allele frequencies, presumably reflecting the history of diseases to which that population has been exposed (Figure 2.1).

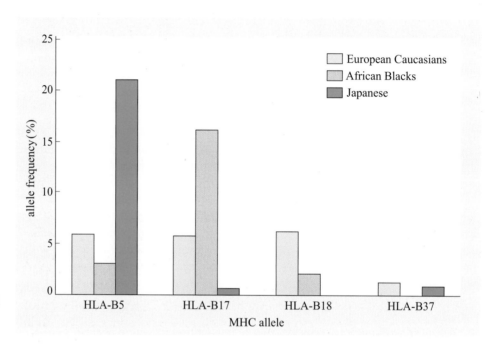

FIGURE 2.1
Percentage allele frequency for selected MHC variants in different human populations.

The MHC was originally discovered in the context of graft rejection. Tissue grafts are much more likely to be successful when donor and recipient have very similar MHC genotypes, and this is more likely when they are close relatives. Genetic variation in the MHC is interpreted as an adaptation against pathogens; over a number of progeny, it allows recognition by the immune system of a wide range of pathogens (see Book 3, Chapter 5). A consequence of the very high levels of variation that exist at MHC loci is that there is a great deal of variation in the effectiveness with which individuals respond to specific pathogens.

If genetic variation in the MHC is an adaptation against pathogens, then we would expect to find hosts to be more susceptible to pathogens if, for some reason, that genetic variation is reduced.

○ Can you suggest a process that tends to reduce genetic variation?

● Inbreeding. Frequent matings among close relatives lead to a reduction in heterozygosity, i.e. reduced genetic variation.

This hypothesis has been tested among free-ranging Soay sheep living on the Scottish island of St. Kilda. Because the size of the sheep population is restricted by the small size of the island, the level of inbreeding is quite high. The study revealed that, in winters when particularly severe weather caused high mortality, the sheep that died had higher levels of intestinal nematode pathogens and were also more inbred than those that survived. What is unclear is the extent to which the homozygosity or the increased parasite burden (possibly caused by the former) contributed to the lower survival.

The very high levels of variation that exist at loci associated with immune defence are paradoxical. Infectious disease exerts strong selection on host populations and the usual outcome of strong selection is very low levels of genetic variation. However, in this case we should not consider 'infectious disease' as a single entity. Each infection is different and requires a different means of recognition (antigen presentation) and response. Consequently, different pathogens select for different genes and therefore promote diversity. The severity of specific disease outbreaks also varies from generation to generation. As a result, strong selection by one pathogen is not sustained for long enough to drive alleles related to that disease to fixation. The 'selective environment' presented by disease is constantly shifting and much of the genetic variation we observe among hosts reflects the exposure of past generations to infections.

There are a number of other factors that may promote high genetic variation in hosts, including:

1 Pathogens selectively infect commoner genotypes so that rare genotypes escape infection and thus tend to increase in frequency. For example, rare genotypes of the New Zealand snail *Potamopyrgus antipodarum* largely escape infection by the trematode *Microphallus*.

2 A number of species, including humans, have been found to mate preferentially with partners who are different from them at MHC loci (a mating pattern called disassortative mating). This increases heterozygosity at MHC loci. Experimental studies using mice provide evidence that MHC heterozygosity is adaptive. Mice were exposed to multiple strains of *Salmonella* and a single strain of *Listeria* in large population enclosures. MHC heterozygous mice had greater survival and higher body weight than homozygous mice.

3 Selection, as in the case of the Soay sheep described above, may act against homozygous individuals.

4 Migration of individuals from one part of a host's range to another introduces novel alleles into local populations. People are particularly mobile hosts and levels of genetic variation in human populations due to migration are thought to be very high.

As a result of all these factors, the human genome is far from static over time; indeed, in terms of allele frequencies in local populations, it is in a constant state of flux.

> Genomes change. Different versions of genes rise and fall in popularity driven by the rise and fall of diseases. ... The genome that we decipher in this generation is but a snapshot of an ever-changing document. There is no definitive edition.
>
> (Ridley, 1999)

Because humans reproduce sexually, we tend to assume that sexual reproduction is the 'normal' way to reproduce. It is, however, only one of many reproductive mechanisms found among animals and plants and its evolution is a matter of continuing debate among evolutionary biologists. This debate arises because sexual reproduction is metabolically very costly, for reasons we cannot explore here. To offset these costs, sexual reproduction must confer some very significant advantage.

> Sex must be important, simply because reproducing in this eccentric way is so expensive. By becoming involved with a male, a female dilutes her genes with those of someone else who does rather little to ensure that they survive. Even worse, she produces sons who go in for the same selfish behaviour. To balance this enormous cost, sex must have some hefty advantages for genes if not for their products – and it does; for a sexual world has conquered death.

(Jones, 1999, p. 272)

Jones is referring to the capacity of sexual reproduction to act as a filter of germ cells that eliminates the majority of mutations before they can be passed on to progeny. But this is only one reason why sex is advantageous. It is widely accepted that another important advantage is that the genetic recombination that results from sex enables a species to counteract pathogens that cause infectious disease. Evidence that pathogens may play a role in determining the reproductive mode of hosts comes from studies of the freshwater snail *Potamopyrgus antipodarum* in New Zealand lakes. Individual snails are either male or female, unlike many snails that are hermaphrodites, but females are capable of a form of asexual reproduction called parthenogenesis (meaning 'virgin birth'). Some populations consist entirely of females and so must reproduce asexually; others contain as many as 40% male individuals, and so have the potential for sexual reproduction. A comparison of 66 snail populations revealed a strong tendency for males to be more frequent in locations that were heavily infected by parasitic trematode flatworms (Figure 2.2). This suggests that sexual reproduction is favoured in snail populations where pathogens are abundant.

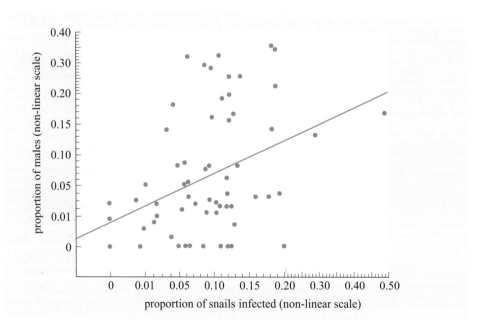

FIGURE 2.2
The relationship between the frequency of males in each population of host snails (*Potamopyrgus antipodarum*) and the proportion infected with parasites.

Sexual reproduction is a complex process that confers many diverse benefits on individuals, but which also incurs many diverse costs. Its role in generating genetic variation as a defence against disease is only one benefit. An important cost is that it provides a very reliable and efficient means of transmission for pathogens, a topic to which we return in Section 2.5. An interesting benefit, relevant to infectious disease, is the opportunity it provides for individuals to mate preferentially with apparently disease-free partners.

2.2.2 Variation and reproduction in pathogens

Like hosts, pathogens show genetic variation that results from mutation and drift, but they vary in terms of the amount of variation resulting from reproduction. Typically, viruses and bacteria reproduce asexually, but protoctists and invertebrate pathogens possess various forms of sexual reproduction that increases genetic variation, as it does for hosts. For example, many tapeworms, which have a very small chance of encountering a mate, may be self-fertilizing hermaphrodites. A survey of pathogens found that sexual reproduction is more common in parasitic species than it is in closely related non-parasitic species and models of coevolution suggest that, under certain conditions, sexual reproduction is adaptive for pathogens.

Although most bacteria do not engage in sexual reproduction, there is increasing evidence that they achieve higher levels of genetic recombination than has generally been assumed. A review of reproductive mechanisms among pathogenic protoctists suggests that most can reproduce sexually, thereby rapidly generating genetic variation, and clonally (i.e. asexually), thereby stabilizing successful genotypes. The mechanisms that cause a protoctist pathogen to switch from one reproductive mode to another are not known.

As we saw in Book 2, a source of genetic variation that sets viruses and bacteria apart from other pathogens is **horizontal transfer** of genes from a variety of sources. Viruses can acquire genes from other viral strains and from host cells. Bacteria can incorporate into their genomes a variety of genetic elements, including plasmids, phages and transposons that may be derived from their environment or from bacteria of other strains or 'species' (Book 2, Box 2.2). The details of these mechanisms are beyond the scope of this book; the significant point is that viruses and bacteria have many ways of acquiring genes from a variety of sources, and thus have the capacity for generating a very high level of genetic variation.

Of particular interest in the context of host/pathogen relationships are genetic elements called pathogenicity islands (PAIs).

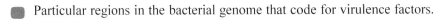

○ Recall from Book 2, p. 33, the definition of pathogenicity islands.

● Particular regions in the bacterial genome that code for virulence factors.

PAIs are large regions of a bacterial genome that are present in the genomes of pathogenic strains but absent from the genomes of the same or related non-pathogenic bacterial species. They are transferred horizontally among bacteria and identical PAIs have been found in bacteria that cause different diseases. They can influence the virulence of a bacteria in a variety of ways, for example, by coding for toxin production (see Section 2.3 for discussion of virulence). PAIs have only recently been discovered and important questions about them are still to be answered, such as: where do they come from and what kind of selective processes are involved in their transfer?.

Largely as a result of the development of modern molecular techniques, biologists are now much more aware of the extent, and the causes, of genetic variation in pathogens than they were some 20 years ago. Previously, pathogens were assumed to conform to a 'clonal model' in which a successful strain could spread through a host population, reproducing asexually, and remaining little changed genetically. It is now realized that, in many pathogens, new strains can appear very frequently because they have ways of generating genetic variation that had not previously been appreciated (see above). One consequence of this is that a single host individual may be host to more than one pathogen strain at the same time. Such within-host variation has important consequences for the severity of illness experienced by hosts. Experimental studies have compared the effect of injecting mice with *Plasmodium* cultures of single and of mixed genotypes. The immune response that mice have to mount against mixed genotype pathogens is more costly and they suffer more severe sickness than when injected with a single genotype. More significantly, the occurrence of within-host variation has completely altered the way in which biologists now view the evolution of a very important aspect of pathogens – their virulence (Section 2.3).

As the number of pathogens whose genomes have been sequenced increases, it becomes apparent that some microbes are more variable than others. Very high levels of genetic variation have been found among samples of *Escherichia coli*, *Helicobacter pylori* and *Staphylococcus* sp., but very little variation has been found among samples of *Mycobacterium tuberculosis*. In contrast to the other species, the genome of *M. tuberculosis* shows very little evidence for the acquisition of new alleles by recombination or by horizontal transfer. High variation is related to pathogen versatility; some *Staphylococcus* species, for example, cause many kinds of disease in many different host species.

2.2.3 HIV

The capacity of pathogens to generate very high levels of genetic variation is strikingly illustrated by HIV. You will recall that HIV is an RNA virus. RNA is intrinsically less stable than DNA, both because it breaks more often and because DNA can be repaired using a complementary strand absent in RNA.

☐ Recall from Book 2 the peculiar feature of RNA replication in HIV (e.g. see Section 3.3.2).

⬤ HIV is a retrovirus which means that DNA can be produced from its RNA template using reverse transcriptase.

Reverse transcriptase has a high error rate, leading to base substitutions, insertions or deletions (see Screen 49 on the 'Biology of HIV' in the *HIV/AIDS* CD-ROM). The consequence is that on average there is about one mutation per genome in every replication cycle. Furthermore, recombination may occur between the two RNA strands in the HIV virus.

☐ What do you predict is the consequence of the high mutation rate and the recombination between strands?

■ It will lead to high genetic variation in the virus.

Because HIV is able to replicate very rapidly, the genetic diversity is apparent even within a single host.

▢ Can you recall another feature of HIV that is particularly relevant here?

■ It has an extremely long period of infectivity, which can be as much as 10 to 15 years. Therefore, HIV has a very long time within a host in which to reproduce and generate variation.

When HIV infects a person, it reproduces and migrates to different parts of the body, especially to the lymph nodes. As a result, several sub-populations are formed which are largely physically isolated from one another. This situation is very similar to the distribution of many animals and plants in fragmented landscapes and, in the language of ecology, is called a **metapopulation** (a population of populations). Each sub-population may differ genetically from the others from the start, because of genetic drift, and, as repr____ _____ nt
more and more over time. A _____ HIV + Coevolution _____
parts of a single dead person _____
between different sub-popula_____ hese
genetic differences revealed _____
chimpanzees; the latter havin_____ tion
is much greater in HIV-1, wl_____ ,
than in HIV-2. Twenty-four _____ 1ad
been identified by 2002.

This example raises an impo_____ nent
that hosts provide for patho_____ s 'we
and other mammals … are li_____ edia'
but, in reality, the host envir_____
organism like a human provi_____ ch
can be regarded as a numbe_____ ıre
specialized to colonize only _____
respiratory tract), but some _____
different parts of a host's body by a pathogen has two important potential consequences:

1   As in the example of HIV described above, it can lead to the pathogen population forming a metapopulation structure with consequent considerable genetic variation.

2   A particular pathogen may have very different effects on its host, depending on which part it has colonized. For example, *Neisseria meningitidis* is typically a commensal inhabitant of the upper respiratory tract, but is a highly virulent pathogen when it crosses into the brain, causing meningitis.

2.2.4 Conclusion

We have noted that coevolution between hosts and pathogens is a process in which each partner is adapted to counteract the adverse effects on it caused by the other. This is a process that may never reach a stable or static outcome.

▢   What is the hypothesis that suggests that coevolved organisms are in a state of continuous evolution?

◼   The Red Queen hypothesis (Book 2, Section 7.6).

Thus, both partners are constantly generating genetic variation. For either partner to continue to exist, it must continually counteract the genetic changes that arise in the other. An important feature of the coevolutionary relationship between hosts and pathogens is that it involves partners that differ, sometimes markedly, in the mechanisms that each possesses for generating genetic variation. They also differ markedly in another important respect – generation time. Because genetic variation largely arises from, and can only be passed on during, reproduction, it follows that the rate at which an organism can generate new genetic variants depends on its rate of reproduction, which is determined by its generation time. Humans have a generation time measured in years; many pathogens have generation times measured in hours or a few days. It follows that pathogens can, potentially, generate new genetic variants at a much higher rate than their hosts.

Summary of Sections 2.1 and 2.2

1   Three models of host–pathogen coevolution are presented: Mutual Aggression (host and pathogen engaged in arms race); Prudent Pathogen (pathogen evolves towards doing less harm to host) and Incipient Mutualism (where pathogen and host come to benefit each other).

2   Genetic variation amongst hosts is one reason for variation in susceptibility to infection. This is illustrated by alleles associated with malaria defence and infection with HIV. The most variable region of the mammalian genome is the major histocompatibility complex (MHC).

3   Genetic variation in hosts may be decreased by inbreeding, which may reduce resistance to disease. Conversely, genetic variation in hosts may be increased by pathogens due to selective infection of commoner genotypes, preferential mating with partners with different MHC loci, temporal variation in the pathogen environment and selection against homozygotes.

4   Genetic variation in pathogens is generated, as in the hosts, by sexual reproduction (amongst protoctists and invertebrate pathogens) and, unlike the hosts, by horizontal transfer of genes (bacteria and viruses). A single host may possess several pathogen strains at one time, exemplified by HIV. Pathogens vary greatly in their genetic variation (e.g. high in *Staphylococcus aureus* and low in *Mycobacterium tuberculosis*).

5   HIV provides a good example of a pathogen that has high genetic variation both within and between hosts. The variation is generated by copying errors by reverse transcriptase and recombination between the RNA strands. This variation is realized within hosts due to the rapid replication of the virus and may be patchy due to the movement of the viruses to different parts of the host, creating a metapopulation structure.

6   The relatively short generation times of pathogens and their high capacity for genetic variation pose a major problem for hosts with long generation times.

2.3 The evolution of virulence

The mechanisms that determine the virulence of a particular pathogen, and the evolutionary factors that determine how virulent it is, are topics of considerable interest.

○ Recall from Books 1 and 2 the meaning of virulence.

● In Book 1, it is a bold term with a concise definition concerning ability to establish an infection. In Book 2, virulence is described as a measure of the ease with which an organism is able to cause damage and disease in host tissues. Bacterial products that contribute to virulence are termed virulence factors.

Thus, the term virulence is being used to cover both the ease with which an infection is established and the degree of damage. Elsewhere, the former definition of virulence is sometimes replaced by the term **infectivity**, which refers to the capacity of a pathogen to infect new hosts, rather than the harm that it does to its host.

Once the pathogen has been transmitted, a major factor determining the virulence of a pathogen is its reproductive rate, as it is by reproducing in host cells that pathogens establish infection and cause damage to host tissues. In other words, virulence can be regarded as 'collateral damage' of pathogen reproduction. This is an important point about the pathogen–host relationship and is crucial for understanding the evolution of virulence. Unlike predators, pathogens are generally not specifically adapted to kill their hosts, but may be adapted to reproduce rapidly. To understand the evolution of virulence, therefore, we need to consider how natural selection acts, not on virulence *per se*, but on characteristics such as the reproductive rate of a pathogen. This raises an important point about the analysis of evolutionary processes, which was emphasized by the late Stephen Jay Gould. Just because a particular character of an organism, such as the virulence of a pathogen, is of interest to us, it does not follow that it is a character that has been subjected directly to natural selection. It may either be a combination of traits or it may be the result of 'coincidental evolution' resulting from natural selection acting on another character. For example, bacteria such as *Clostridium botulinum*, which causes botulism, and *C. tetani*, which causes tetanus, produce powerful toxins that attack the nervous system, making them very dangerous to humans. Neither pathogen is transmitted from human to human; both are better regarded as soil-living bacteria that can infect humans. (Neonatal tetanus is a major global problem, causing about 500 000 deaths per year.) It is thus likely that their toxins have evolved in the context of their normal, soil (or sausage!)-living existence and that their pathogenicity in humans is coincidental.

All other things being equal, natural selection favours those pathogen strains that reproduce most rapidly because they leave more progeny. There are circumstances, however, in which slower pathogen reproduction is favoured by natural selection because the host lives for longer. There is thus a trade-off between rapid reproduction and host survival, that is between high and low pathogen virulence.

The above definitions of virulence of a pathogen are useful as qualitative descriptions but need to be quantified for formulating mathematical models of the epidemiology or evolution of disease. In studies using animals, the virulence of a pathogen is expressed as its lethal dose (LD_{50}), the number of microbes required to kill 50% of infected hosts. In human studies, it is expressed as the case fatality rate, the number of infected individuals who die divided by the number of individuals infected, usually expressed as a percentage. The case fatality rate of diarrhoeal diseases is 5 or 6% (death rates in children are much higher), cholera 5–50% (depending on treatment) and AIDS at least 90%. These definitions measure virulence in terms of host mortality, and thus provide convenient, explicit and quantifiable measures that can be used in mathematical models. They ignore, however, many aspects of the harm that pathogens do to their hosts that do not involve death, but which can be considered to be aspects of virulence, such as how incapacitated does a host become.

When thinking about the evolutionary biology of infectious diseases, we need to define virulence in terms of host fitness; the virulence of a pathogen is the reduction in the fitness of a host that results from infection by that pathogen. This definition is also problematic for two reasons. First, fitness is very difficult to measure and, secondly, as emphasized in Section 2.2, individual hosts vary considerably in their response to infection by a particular pathogen, which creates a problem for all definitions of virulence. Virulence is not a fixed property of a given pathogen but is a dynamic property of the interaction between host and pathogen, changing over time. For example, syphilis in Europe may have been a much more severe disease in the 16th century, killing people within months rather than years.

○ What problem for this interpretation is highlighted by the *Syphilis* Case Study?

● It raises the debate as to whether 'the Great Pox' was actually syphilis or another disease or even a cocktail of diseases (possibly including syphilis).

Scarlet fever, caused by the bacterium *Streptococcus pyogenes*, was a disease with a very high case fatality rate in the late 1800s, killing very large numbers of children, but by the 1930s and 1940s it had become a relatively mild childhood disease. This may in part have been due to its development of effective treatments. Influenza is the best-known example of a disease in which periodic outbreaks are caused by the emergence of especially virulent viral strains, the most recent being the 1918 pandemic (Book 1, Chapter 2).

FIGURE 2.3
Rabbit infected with the *Myxoma* virus.

The idea that some diseases may have been more severe in the past is often used as evidence that there is a general evolutionary trend by which virulent pathogens become more benign. Further evidence for such a process comes from the history of myxomatosis in Australia, a rare example in which evolutionary change in a disease was directly observed over several years. The *Myxoma* virus is indigenous to South America, where it causes a non-lethal disease in rabbits. In 1950 it was introduced to Australia in an attempt to control massive populations of rabbits, themselves introduced from Europe. A flea-borne pathogen, the *Myxoma* virus caused an epidemic that killed 99.8% of rabbits (Figure 2.3). A second epidemic killed 90% of the rabbit generation that resulted from the survivors of the first, but a third epidemic killed only 50%. This rapid change was due in part to a decrease in the virulence of the virus, in part to rapidly evolving immune defences among the rabbits. So prevalent is the idea that pathogens generally evolve from being very virulent towards being benign that it has been referred to as the 'conventional wisdom'. The emphasis of much of the recent literature in this area is to challenge this view, and to identify the circumstances in which it is and is not true.

Venereal syphilis is an example of a disease that may have evolved from one of two milder diseases – pinta and yaws. There is fairly general acceptance that pinta and yaws existed among humans long before syphilis evolved. One theory for the origin of syphilis is that it followed the early transition of human societies from a purely rural existence to urban life. One suggestion is that the pathogen evolved into a venereal pathogen when the wearing of clothes reduced the frequency of the skin-to-skin contact by which yaws and pinta are transmitted. As a result, a mild disease of children evolved into a severe disease of adults.

○   Based on the pathogen life-history strategies in Table 1.4, what would you predict about the duration of yaws and pinta in the host if the frequency of skin-to-skin contact is higher than for syphilis.

●   The pathogens of these species would be expected to have shorter durations in the host. This appears to be true, although yaws may remain in the host for up to 10 years (pinta has a much shorter duration in the host).

Another example is provided by detailed genetic analysis of the plague pathogen *Yersinia pestis*, that suggests it evolved from the much less virulent *Y. pseudotuberculosis*, a human enteric pathogen. However, we need to be wary about distinguishing between evolution of new strains or species with increased or decreased virulence and evolution of more or less virulence within a strain or species.

In Book 2, it was noted that the virulence of bacteria is determined by a number of specific aspects of its biology, called virulence factors, often determined by genes derived by horizontal transfer. These virulence factors include the effectiveness of the bacterial pathogen in penetrating host cells, how successfully they evade their host's immune system, and their ability to obtain essential nutrients, particularly iron, from its host. (Such arguments about virulence factors can also be applied to pathogens other than bacteria.) A recent discovery suggests that at least one virulence factor, colonization of the host, can change very rapidly. Cultures of the cholera pathogen *Vibrio cholerae* collected from pond water are less infectious than cultures collected from human faeces; passage through the gut of a human host induces a change in the bacterium that makes it more infectious. This change involves the activation of *V. cholera* genes that are not expressed in pond water. In experiments using mice as hosts, cholera bacteria collected from human faeces were 700 times more infectious than bacteria collected from laboratory cultures. This hyperinfectivity lasts for at least five hours in pond water, but disappears in bacteria kept for 18 hours in the laboratory. The mechanism underlying hyperinfectivity may help explain why it is that cholera epidemics spread very rapidly.

Finally, it is important to consider that the virulence of a pathogen with respect to a particular host depends on whether or not that pathogen has alternative hosts. For such pathogens, it may be entirely inappropriate to consider virulence with respect to humans as being subject to natural selection in humans at all. Some of the deadliest human infectious diseases are caused by pathogens whose natural hosts are other mammals or birds, e.g. Ebola fever and hantavirus. For these diseases, virulence in humans appears to be much greater than it is in their non-human hosts and is best regarded, not as an adaptation by a pathogen to human hosts, but as a by-product of its coevolution with its non-human hosts.

> A truly successful pathogen is commensal, living in amity with its host, or even giving it positive advantages … A pathogen that regularly and inevitably kills its hosts cannot survive long, in the evolutionary sense, unless it multiplies with tremendous rapidity.
>
> (Mr Spock, *Star Trek 2*)

Summary of Section 2.3

1   Virulence has been defined as both the ease with which an infection is established and the degree of damage. The best definition from an evolutionary point of view is effect on host fitness, but this is difficult to measure.

2   Virulence can be thought of as collateral damage of pathogen reproduction. As such, evolution of virulence may be misleading and we should be considering evolution of reproduction rates.

3   Quantitative definitions of virulence include lethal dose and case fatality rate.

4   Conventional wisdom is that pathogens evolve from more to less virulent. However, there are counter-examples, especially in the initial stages of pathogen evolution (e.g. *Yersinia* species). What is certain is that virulence factors may change rapidly, e.g. as in cholera.

2.4 Manipulation of hosts by pathogens

2.4.1 Introduction

Crickets are terrestrial animals that normally avoid water. Individuals infected with hairworms (genus *Nematomorpha*), however, hurl themselves into ponds and streams, where they are eaten by fish. This is but one example of manipulation of host behaviour by a pathogen. The host's behaviour is maladaptive for itself but is adaptive for the pathogen; in this example, fish are the final hosts and crickets an intermediate host for the pathogen. Many examples of **host manipulation** involve pathogens with complex life cycles, in which it is the behaviour of an intermediate host that is manipulated in such a way that the chances of the pathogen's life cycle being completed are increased (see Table 2.1 and Figure 2.4).

○   Recall from Book 2 an example of manipulation of hosts by pathogens.

●   The liver fluke *Dicrocoelium dendriticum* that affects the behaviour of its intermediate ant host (Book 2, Chapter 7).

TABLE 2.1 Manipulation of hosts or vectors by parasites/pathogens.

Host or vectors	Parasite/pathogen	Nature of manipulation
beetle, *Tenebrio monitor* (final host is rat)	tapeworm, *Hymenolepis diminuta*	infected beetles invest less in reproduction and consequently survive longer (40% increase in survival time in females, 25% in males)
mammals	rabies virus	infected host develops rabid behaviour, which includes intense salivation and tendency to bite other animals
snail, *Succinea* (final host is bird)	trematode, *Leucochloridium macrostomum*	parasite sporocysts invade snail's tentacles, causing them to swell, making snail very conspicuous to birds and thus more likely to be eaten (see Figure 2.4)
banded killifish, *Fundulus diaphanus* (final host is bird)	digenean trematode, *Crassiphiala bulboglossa*	parasitized fish are hungry, move to periphery of shoal to find food, more likely to be eaten by birds
mosquito	malaria pathogen, *Plasmodium* sp.	infected mosquitoes continue feeding throughout the night, whereas uninfected ones do not; as a result, infected mosquitoes bite more hosts

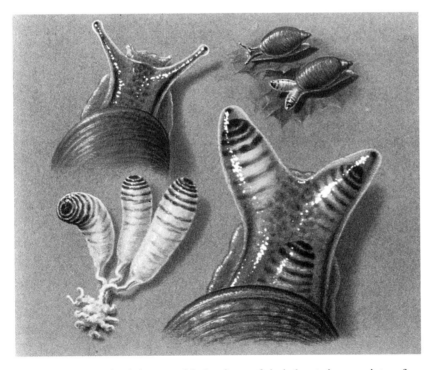

FIGURE 2.4
Manipulation of its host by a pathogen. The snail (*Succinea*, top left) is the intermediate host of the bird trematode *Leucochloridium macrostomum*. Reproduction in the snail produces large sporocysts (lower left) that migrate into the snail's tentacles, making them very swollen (lower right). These are very conspicuous (top right) to birds which bite them off the snail, thus becoming infected.

Pathogens affect the physiology and behaviour of their hosts in a variety of ways. In the context of human diseases, these changes, such as sneezing or diarrhoea, are generally regarded as symptoms. There are three ways of looking at these:

1 they are incidental consequences of infection, and are of no functional significance to either host or pathogen;

2 they are adaptive, defensive reactions to infection by the host;

3 they are changes in the host caused by pathogen manipulation and are adaptive for the pathogen, e.g. in aiding transmission.

Categories 2 and 3 are not mutually exclusive – it is possible for a change in a host to be adaptive for the host and to be adaptive for a pathogen (see below).

The possibility that symptoms of disease may be adaptive responses on the part of the host belongs to an area of biology called evolutionary medicine, which was pioneered by Randolph Nesse and George Williams. This takes the view that symptoms of disease such as pain, coughing, nausea, vomiting, diarrhoea and fever are defensive responses by the host that reduce the impact of infection. Vomiting and diarrhoea are mechanisms that eliminate pathogens from the body quickly; fever changes the host's body temperature in a way that favours the host's defence systems over the pathogen.

This way of viewing the world of infectious diseases raises a lot of interesting ideas but is fraught with pitfalls. A problem with evolutionary theory is that it can be used to explain everything by applying the general argument that 'if it exists it must be adaptive'. This does not advance our scientific understanding. Explanations that invoke adaptation should be regarded as hypotheses that can be rigorously tested. If we wanted to test the hypothesis that vomiting is an adaptive response to infection, for example, we would need to find a way of preventing it and then seeing if subjects become more ill as a result. There have been very few rigorous tests of ideas put forward under the heading of evolutionary medicine and so, for the present, it is best regarded as an interesting alternative way at looking at some aspects of infectious disease.

2.4.2 *Wolbachia*

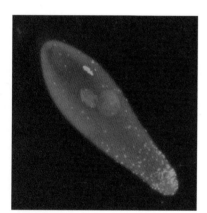

FIGURE 2.5
Electron micrograph of *Wolbachia*.

A remarkable form of host manipulation by symbiotic microbes is shown by rickettsial bacteria of the genus ***Wolbachia***. These infect arthropods and nematode worms (and may infect other invertebrate species) and are primarily transmitted vertically in the cytoplasm of host eggs, but can also be transmitted horizontally, sometimes between host species. In line with the general prediction that vertically transmitted symbionts will be benign or mutualistic, they are generally not virulent and, indeed, there are cases where they enhance host fecundity. However, the fact that they are transmitted exclusively through host females means that they are very hostile to males of host species. Some *Wolbachia* species kill male host embryos, others render sperm incompatible with uninfected eggs and others cause males to become females. In some host species, normally sexually reproducing females become parthenogenetic as a result of *Wolbachia* infection, rendering host males redundant.

Research into *Wolbachia* is at such an early stage that it is not clear how diverse it is, in terms of numbers of 'species', nor how wide is its range of hosts. In 1997 it was estimated to be present in 15 to 20% of all insect species, but by 2001 it was thought to be present in 75% of all arthropods! Although usually benign, at least to female hosts, some forms of *Wolbachia* are highly virulent. A strain found in *Drosophila*, charmingly called 'popcorn', becomes active as its host reaches maturity and kills it before it reproduces.

Research into *Wolbachia* has increased greatly in recent years, much of it driven by the possibility that *Wolbachia* could be used as a means to control insect pests, including disease vectors. For example, research is currently under way to see if *Wolbachia* can be used to control tsetse flies.

The human disease river blindness (onchocerciasis) is caused by the insect-borne nematode *Onchocerca volvulus* (Book 2, Section 7.5.2). It has recently been discovered that the immune reaction in the cornea that leads to blindness is not due to the nematode itself, but to endosymbiotic *Wolbachia* in the nematode. Treating the nematode with antibiotics eliminates the *Wolbachia*; it no longer causes blindness and, furthermore, becomes sterile.

2.4.3 Fever

Increased body temperature is a common symptom of infectious disease. There has long been a debate as to whether fever is an example of host manipulation by pathogens or is an adaptive response by the host. This question has been addressed experimentally in reptiles, and mammals, such as rabbits. Reptiles are ectotherms, meaning that they acquire body heat from their external environment, moving to warmer places to raise their body temperature; mammals are endotherms, generating heat internally. With reptiles, it is relatively easy to experimentally change their body temperature, by simply controlling the temperature of their environment. Several studies of this kind have shown that the survival of infected animals is increased if their body temperature is raised. With mammals, the most commonly used experimental approach is to suppress the physiological responses that cause fever; many such studies have shown that this procedure reduces the survival of infected animals.

At one time, it was thought that fever acts as a defence against infection by suppressing bacterial or viral reproduction, but this is not usually the case. Rather, it seems to enhance certain aspects of the host's immune response, e.g. increasing the rate of lymphocyte division. In particular, it acts synergistically with the host's physiological mechanisms that reduce the amount of iron circulating in the body. Iron is vital for microbe reproduction and denying them access to it reduces their reproductive rate.

Views on the importance of host manipulation as an outcome of the coevolution of hosts and pathogens are varied, and have shifted over the years. Examples like those listed in Table 2.1, which mostly relate to the manipulation of intermediate rather than final hosts, lead some researchers to see manipulation as a general characteristic of pathogens. A detailed analysis of the literature by Poulin, published in 2000, however, showed that the concept of host manipulation was a 'weakening paradigm'. On the other hand, it appears that the concept of host manipulation is staging a revival, primarily as the result of new discoveries about the very intimate ways in which pathogens interact, at a sub-cellular level, with their hosts. These ways include the process of apoptosis (Book 2, p. 81) in which the response of hosts to infection is to selectively kill off infected cells. As might be predicted from coevolution, some pathogens can prevent this threat to their survival by switching apoptosis off, for example, cytomegalovirus (CMV).

Summary of Section 2.4

1   There are three interpretations of changes in host behaviour and/or physiology due to pathogens. First, as incidental consequences of pathogens, secondly as adaptive defensive reactions by the host and thirdly as changes which favour the pathogen, e.g. in transmission.

2   *Wolbachia* bacteria manipulate their invertebrate host species by killing or harming males or removing the need for males by causing females to reproduce parthenogenetically.

3   The role of fever as either host manipulation or adaptive response of hosts has been tested experimentally. These studies have shown that fever increases host survival, probably by enhancing the immune response.

2.5 Evolution of transmission mechanisms

In Chapter 1, we emphasized the importance of transmission of pathogens in its relationship to within-host processes (Table 1.4), recognizing three routes of transmission. In this chapter, we have also discussed the importance of transmission with regard to virulence. It is therefore appropriate to spend some time discussing evolutionary aspects of transmission, focusing on two of the transmission types in Table 1.4: host-to-host contact and vectors. This will set the scene for discussion of related ecological aspects of transmission in Chapter 3.

2.5.1 Sexually transmitted infections

Sexually transmitted infections (STIs) are caused by pathogens whose principal means of transmission from one host to another is sexual intercourse by the host. This is a somewhat loose definition; some STIs can be transmitted in other ways (e.g. HIV by sharing hypodermic needles or blood transfusion). In addition to horizontal transmission during sex, many STIs are also transmitted vertically, either to the foetus in the uterus, or during birth, as the baby passes through the infected vagina. Whilst more than 20 pathogens may be transmitted during sex in humans (WHO Department of HIV/AIDS), we are only beginning to appreciate the diversity of STIs among other host species (see below).

Examples of the diversity of human STIs are given in Table 2.2. They typically cause chronic symptoms (see definition in Book 1, p. 21), for reasons we will explore, and, with the exception of HIV, cause relatively low mortality. WHO estimated that 174 million new cases of three STIs, gonorrhoea, syphilis and trichomoniasis, occurred worldwide in 1999 in men and women aged 15 to 49 years (WHO Department of HIV/AIDS). At the end of 2001, 40 million people were infected with HIV, with 5 million new cases occurring in 2001 ('HIV' lecture on the *Immunology* CD2). STIs are a major cause of infertility in women and when transmitted vertically to infants they often have much more serious effects than they do in adults. They are also associated with a greatly increased risk of HIV infection: people with gonorrhoea have a three-fold increased risk of contracting HIV, people with syphilis a four-fold increased risk (see *Syphilis* Case Study). The causal basis of this effect is not fully understood but is likely to involve several factors; for example, the genital lesions caused by STIs may make people more likely to be infected by HIV.

It is not surprising that many pathogens exploit host sexual activity as a means of transmission; it is a very intimate form of contact, ensuring reliable transmission and, for many species, it is the only context in which hosts come close enough for transmission to occur.

☐   What other advantage does transmission by sexual contact provide for the pathogen?

TABLE 2.2 Sexually transmitted infections of global importance.

Disease	Pathogen	Incidence*	Comments
syphilis	spirochaete bacterium *Treponema pallidum*	estimated 24 million new cases worldwide in 1999	can cause abortion, premature delivery, stillbirth; other symptoms detailed in *Syphilis Case Study*
gonorrhoea	coccal bacterium *Neisseria gonorrhoeae*	estimated 62 million new cases worldwide in 1999	common cause of pelvic inflammatory disease with subsequent risk of infertility; vertical transmission to infants causes blindness
genital herpes	herpes simplex virus 2 (HSV2)	approximately one-fifth of US adult population infected in late 20th century	closely related HSV1 causes oral herpes (cold sores)
AIDS	HIV	estimated that about 5 million new cases occur worldwide every year	see *HIV/AIDS Case Study*
chlamydia	bacterium *Chlamydia trachomatis*	estimated 92 million new cases worldwide in 1999	common cause of pelvic inflammatory disease with subsequent risk of infertility; vertical transmission causes conjunctivitis, blindness, pneumonia in infants
trichomoniasis	flagellate protoctist *Trichomonas vaginalis*	estimated 88 million new cases worldwide in 1999	affects women; men are asymptomatic carriers; associated with premature birth and low birth weight; may facilitate spread of HIV
candidiasis (thrush)	yeast *Candida albicans*	extremely common	see Book 2, p. 117

Source: WHO Department of HIV/AIDS.

● It guarantees transmission to another member of the same species (normally!), i.e. it provides host specificity.

Thus there is little or no opportunity for STIs to be transmitted between species. As a result, STIs are typically species-specific and we do not have to consider other host species in the context of controlling them.

STIs share a number of features that can be understood, in evolutionary terms, as adaptations by the pathogens to their mode of transmission. They have a long incubation period and latent period. They typically do not cause debilitating illness, except in very late stages of infection. The host does not develop immunity to them and so can be repeatedly infected.

Consider the host/pathogen relationship from the perspective of a venereal pathogen. The ideal host would be one that mates frequently and with many partners; such host behaviour would maximize its transmission to new hosts. In the real world, however, most hosts do not conform to this ideal. For many species, mating is a rare event and may occur only at certain times of year. There are many species that mate quite often, but do not often change their sexual partner. This is important from the standpoint of a venereal pathogen, because its fitness depends on the number of new hosts infected. In general, therefore, the interval between infection of a new host and that host mating with a new partner is long, much longer than that between catching a cold and starting to sneeze. Were a venereal pathogen to cause a debilitating, acute illness, it would severely reduce its chances of being transmitted to new hosts. Theoretical studies have suggested that, if a venereal pathogen reduces the mating success of its host, selection will favour strains of the pathogen that have reduced virulence. The optimal strategy for a venereal pathogen is thus to minimize the damage it does to its host for as long as possible. Consequently, it has to evade rather than seek to outpace its host's immune defences (see the discussion on pathogen strategies in Chapter 1).

Evasion of host defences involves two possible strategies: finding a place where the immune response is relatively weak, and becoming less detectable by the host's immune system. The genital tract of a female host is a potentially safe place for a pathogen because the host cannot afford defences so effective that they destroy sperm. Herpes viruses, including herpes simplex and herpes zoster, invade the nervous system of their host, a relatively safe site because the host cannot afford to damage nerve cells by mounting a vigorous immune response. There they remain dormant until the host's immune system is compromised by stress or illness. HIV incorporates itself into the cells of the host's immune system. The syphilis bacterium sheds the surface molecules that enable its host to recognize it, and the gonorrhoea bacterium changes its surface molecules so frequently that the host immune response does not catch up. Interestingly, the pilus genes of *Neisseria gonorrhoea* are one of the few places where introns occur in prokaryotic genes. The presence of introns introduces the possibility of varied splicing patterns which may contribute to variation of the *N. gonorrhoea* surface.

Related to the essentially 'stealthy' nature of sexually transmitted pathogens is the fact that many infected people present no symptoms; they are nonetheless able to transmit STIs to others. For example, 70 to 75% of women and 50% of men infected with *Chlamydia trachomatis* are symptom-free; 80% of women and 10% of men infected with gonorrhoea are asymptomatic (WHO Department of HIV/AIDS). This makes efforts to control these diseases very much more difficult.

○ In the context of transmission, how would you interpret the subtle symptoms of first stage syphilis?

◉ This helps transmission by not affecting host sexual behaviour and the pathogen not being detected by the host or potential mates.

It has been suggested that venereal pathogens might have evolved mechanisms by which they manipulate their hosts to mate more often or with more partners. In humans, promiscuity and the incidence of STIs are correlated but there is no reason to suppose that the causal basis of this correlation is anything other than that promiscuous behaviour increases the risk of infection. A few studies of animals have sought evidence that venereal pathogens cause more promiscuous behaviour but none has yet demonstrated such an effect.

Given the enormous variation among animal species in terms of how frequently they mate and, more importantly, how many mating partners they have, comparative studies would provide valuable insights into the impact of these variables on the evolution of host/venereal pathogen relationships. The information that is available for animal STIs has been reviewed by Sheila Lockhart and colleagues. They documented over 200 diseases, spread across a wide diversity of host species and involving a wide variety of pathogens. Among mammals, STIs, in comparison to other diseases, typically cause low mortality, are long-lived in their hosts, invoke relatively weak immune responses, have a narrower range of hosts and show less fluctuation in prevalence over time. This agrees with the observations for human STIs.

Detailed studies have been made of two STIs of the familiar two-spot ladybird (*Adalia bipunctata*). The fungus *Hesperomyces virescens* appears to affect ladybirds only in urban habitats and has been studied in London. Samples of ladybirds taken along transects running north to south and east to west across London show that its prevalence reaches a peak, at 50%, near Euston railway station (Figure 2.6). One possible explanation for this distribution is that higher temperatures in central London increase activity in ladybirds, enabling them to mate more often, and thus with more partners, than in rural habitats.

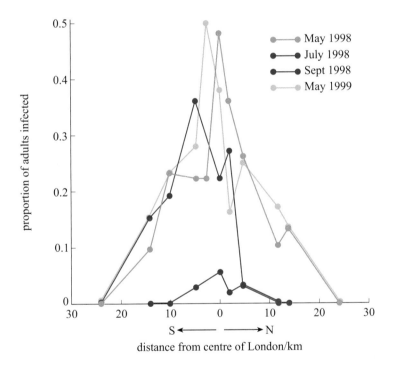

FIGURE 2.6
Prevalence of sexually transmitted disease in ladybirds.

The epidemiology and control of STIs are subject, perhaps more than other diseases, to powerful social factors. First, the social stigma attached to STIs makes infected people very reluctant to report them. Secondly, programmes to control STIs involve intense initiatives to educate people, to improve reporting rates and to carry out contact tracing. Such measures tend to collapse at times of social disruption. There has been a massive increase in the incidence of STIs in Eastern Europe following the break-up of the USSR. Major outbreaks of STIs also occur at times of war; additional factors here are the close association between soldiers and prostitutes and the propensity of invading armies to commit rape.

2.5.2 Vector-borne diseases

You have already studied some of the important infectious diseases of humans transmitted by vectors (see Table 2.3). A vector is a living creature that can transmit infection from one host to another. While vectors are normally considered in the context of transmission from one human host to another, they can also transmit pathogens between different host species and are thus a factor in zoonotic diseases (see Box 1.2 in Book 1). Historically, vector-borne diseases, including malaria, dengue fever, yellow fever and plague, were probably responsible for more human disease and death in the 17th century through to the early 20th century than all other causes combined (although respiratory infections and diarrhoeal diseases, especially amongst babies, may have been as important). The evolutionary biology and ecology of vector-borne diseases is much more complex than that of directly transmitted diseases, because it involves an interaction between three, rather than two partners. We have to consider not only the relationship between pathogen and final host, but also that between pathogen and vector and that between vector and final host.

TABLE 2.3 Arthropod vectors of medical importance.

Arthropod	Diseases transmitted
mosquitoes	malaria, dengue fever, filariasis, yellow fever
sandflies	leishmaniasis, sandfly fever
other flies	trypanosomiasis, onchocerciasis
fleas	plague, rickettsial infection
ticks	relapsing fever, rickettsial infection, Lyme disease
mites	rickettsial infection
lice	relapsing fever, typhus

Insect vectors have been described as 'flying syringes', the implication being that they provide a very reliable mode of pathogen transmission, regardless of the mobility of the human host and one which, moreover, evades many of the host's first-line defences.

Because vector-borne pathogens are dependent on their vector to transmit them to new hosts, it is widely assumed that it is in their best interests not to harm the health of the vector. Insects have complex immune systems, similar in some ways to those of mammals (although insects lack lymphocytes and antibodies) that defend them against pathogenic microbes. Recent research has shown how the insect vector's immune systems respond to the pathogens they carry. For example, mosquitoes mount an immune response to malarial pathogens, indicating that they are not simply passive in transmission. In response, vector-borne pathogens are covered by surface coats that not only protect them from the vector's immune system, but which also interact with specific vector tissues to find those sites in the vector's body where development and reproduction of the pathogen take place. Overall, the question of whether or not malaria pathogens have a harmful effect on their mosquito vectors remains unresolved. The number of studies that have found evidence of detrimental effects is roughly equal to the number that have not. A number of harmful effects of malaria pathogens on mosquitoes have been identified, including tissue damage, loss of protein and glucose to the benefit of pathogens, and an increased risk of death resulting from the fact that infected mosquitoes feed more often and may be more easily swatted!

To be successfully transmitted by a vector, a pathogen must be able to evade or resist defensive responses to it that are made by its vector. Thus, pathogens must acquire adaptations that enable them to be vector-borne. We noted in Section 2.3 that the plague bacillus *Yersinia pestis* evolved relatively recently from *Y. pseudotuberculosis*, which causes a relatively mild food- and water-borne gut disease. Genetic comparison of these two bacteria has revealed that *Y. pestis* differs from *Y. pseudotuberculosis* by the inclusion in the former of two plasmids. One of these codes for an enzyme that protects the bacillus from digestion by its rat flea vector. This ability to be transmitted by a vector may have favoured the evolution of more virulent forms of *Yersinia*, and thus the emergence of plague.

The fact that vectors are not simply passive carriers of pathogens, but have a complex interaction with them, is very important for the development of new control measures for diseases such as malaria. Current efforts to control malaria are hampered by the evolution of drug resistance in *Plasmodium*, the evolution of insecticide resistance in mosquitoes and the lack of an effective vaccine. A potentially effective new tool is to use genetic modification to strengthen the response of mosquitoes to *Plasmodium*. Such genetic modifications have already been achieved, in the laboratory, to produce mosquitoes that are relatively inefficient at transmitting the malaria pathogen. Transferring this technique to the field is fraught with problems however, not least because of public and scientific concerns about the possible long-term effects of releasing genetically modified organisms into the wild.

Recent evidence suggests that the rodent malarial pathogen *Plasmodium berghei* itself limits the degree to which it infects its mosquito vector *Anopheles stephensi*. Only a small proportion of the gametocytes that enter the mosquito's midgut after a blood meal survive. The midgut is a hostile environment for the gametocytes but more than 50% die naturally by apoptosis or programmed cell death. This appears to be an adaptation on the part of the pathogen that limits the burden that it imposes on its mosquito vector. Most significantly, it offers an interesting avenue of research into new ways to control malaria; if mechanisms that can increase the proportion of pathogens that undergo apoptosis can be found, then malarial proliferation in mosquitoes might be reduced.

Some vector-borne diseases are emerging or resurging for a complex variety of reasons. These include urbanization, deforestation and changing agricultural practices, but a major reason is the evolution of drug-resistant pathogen strains and of pesticide resistance in vectors. There are also alarming predictions about the long-term effects of climate change; global warming, it is argued, will cause vectors to expand their range, bringing malaria to temperate regions where currently it cannot survive. The data currently available on the impact of climate change on vector-borne diseases are inconclusive. This should be seen as 'absence of evidence', rather than as 'evidence of absence' for such an effect.

Some emerging infections of humans are primarily diseases of animals that have become more common in recent years because humans have increased their frequency of contact with their vectors. Tick-borne encephalitis and Lyme disease (Book 2, p. 55 and Figure 2.7) have increased in northern temperate regions, including Europe and North America, since the 1980s because of greater human contact with the ticks that transmit them. The incidence of Lyme disease has

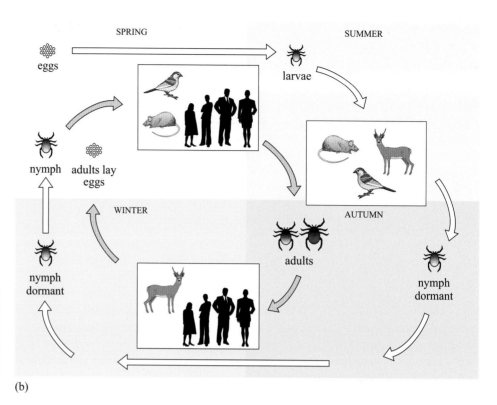

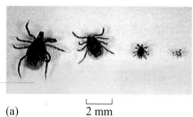

FIGURE 2.7 (a) *Ixodes* sp.: from left to right, adult male and female; two immature stages. (b) The two-year life cycle of a deer tick located in a north-eastern state of the United States. Life cycles may vary slightly for other ticks in different regions of North America. Adult female ticks lay eggs on the ground in early spring. By summer, eggs hatch into larvae. Larvae feed on mice, other small mammals, deer, and birds in the late summer and early autumn, moult into nymphs, and then are dormant until the next spring. Nymphs feed on rodents, other small mammals, birds and humans in the late spring and summer and moult into adults in the autumn. In the autumn and early spring, adult ticks feed and mate on large mammals (especially deer) and bite humans. The adult female ticks then drop off these animals and lay eggs in spring, completing a two-year life cycle.

increased steadily since its discovery in the USA in 1975. In the eastern USA, a lot of farmland has fallen into disuse, encouraging an increase in populations of wild deer, which carry *Ixodes* ticks; humans pick them up from long grass where deer have been grazing.

Finally, the fact that vectors can transmit pathogens between different host species raises the possibility that they have been responsible for the transfer of animal diseases to humans. For example, the blood-sucking stable fly (*Stomoxys calcitrans*) is capable of transmitting HIV and, because it feeds on the carcases of dead apes offered for sale as 'bush meat' in African markets, as well as humans, it may have been the agent that passed HIV from primates to humans.

Summary of Section 2.5

1   The evolutionary aspects of two types of transmission are discussed in detail – transmission by host-to-host contact through sexual activity and transmission by vectors.

2   Sexually transmitted infections (STIs) are caused by viruses, bacteria and fungi and affect large numbers of people worldwide and generally cause chronic infections.

3   STIs are host-specific with the pathogen adopting a strategy of stealth and/or evasion in the host.

4   There is no evidence that sexually transmitted pathogens manipulate their hosts to increase promiscuity.

5   Studies across a wide range of animal species support the idea of STIs as diseases of low mortality (with the exception of HIV), caused by long-lived pathogens with a narrow host range and eliciting weak immune responses.

6   Insect vectors are effectively flying syringes, providing a reliable means of transmission.

7   The immune systems of insect vectors provide defence against the pathogens they carry. In response, the pathogens protect themselves against the vector's immune system.

8   Genetic modification of the insect vector and the discovery of pathogen-induced apoptosis offers hopes of novel methods for controlling malaria.

9   There are various reasons for emerging or resurging vector-borne diseases, including urbanization, deforestation, evolution of drug-resistant pathogens and pesticide-resistant vectors and possibly climate change.

2.6 The evolution of resistance to antibiotics and drugs

> Material on antibiotic resistance, particularly the underlying molecular mechanisms involved, is available in S204, Book 4, Chapter 7 (*Reference* CD-ROM). Also see Book 2, pp. 30–31 for background information on antibiotics.

There is no more striking illustration of the power of natural selection to bring about phenotypic and genotypic change, and to do so very rapidly, than the evolution of bacterial resistance to antibiotics and wider drug resistance in pathogens (introduced in Box 1.4, Book 1). This includes pathogenic fungi that have evolved resistance to antifungal drugs, for example, *Candida* species and drug resistance in *Plasmodium* species.

○   Recall from Book 1, Chapter 1 an example of antibiotic resistance in the bacterium *Staphylococcus aureus*, the most prevalent cause of surgical site infection.

●   Resistance to the antibiotic methicillin, giving rise to methicillin-resistant *Staphylococcus aureus* (MRSA). A survey in 1997–1999 (Table 4.1, Book 1) revealed 61% of such infections were caused by methicillin-resistant strains. Antibiotic resistance is predicted to be a major cause of hospital-acquired infections.

As a result of these evolutionary changes, many of the chemical compounds developed to control pathogens, of which so much was expected 50 years ago, are now totally ineffective. Furthermore, many of the most pathogenic microbes that threaten human health have evolved defences against everything that has been developed to control them. These 'superbugs' pose a major threat to people throughout the world, who are now dying of diseases that could previously be cured.

> The use of antibiotics by humans can be seen as an evolutionary experiment of enormous magnitude, a window from which to view not-quite-natural selection operating in real time. Within 50 years, the number of species and strains of pathogenic and commensal bacteria resistant to antibiotics and the number of antibiotics to which they are resistant has increased virtually monotonically worldwide.
>
> (Anderson and Levin, 1999.)

Pathogenic microbes would very likely have evolved some level of resistance to antibiotics even if they had been used in the most prudent way possible. Indeed, evidence from bacterial collections suggests that antibiotic resistance pre-dates antibiotics! This antibiotic resistance may involve selection of pre-existing traits. The problem has been made much worse, however, by the misuse of antibiotics on a massive scale. In the EU and USA alone, it was estimated in 2002 that 10 000 metric tons of antibiotics are used each year. These have not been used exclusively to directly combat human diseases. It has been estimated that up to 75% of antibiotic use has been of doubtful value in terms of treating human disease (Table 2.4). Only 50% of antibiotic use is to treat illness in people; the other 50% is used in agriculture, to counter animal diseases, as prophylactics and as growth promoters. While the benefits and costs of some of these uses is a matter of debate, there can surely be little doubt that some uses of antibiotics defy common sense. In some parts of the world, antibiotics are sprayed on fruit trees, or poured in large quantities into salmon hatcheries. The major problem with these agricultural uses is that antibiotics get into the soil and into ground water, leading to the evolution of antibiotic resistance in a myriad microbe species that are not pathogens, but which provide a source of resistant genes for those microbes that are.

TABLE 2.4 Summary of uses of antibiotics.

Where antibiotics are used	Types of use	Questionable use
humans (50%)	hospitals (20%) community (80%)	20–50% unnecessary
agriculture (50%)	therapeutic (20%) prophylaxis/growth promotion (80%)	40–80% highly questionable

Antibiotics fed to cattle pass into their faeces, which are then spread as slurry over fields. Even in Switzerland, where the use of antibiotics as growth promoters is prohibited, sulphonamide drugs, which do not degrade quickly, occur in the soil at concentrations up to 1 kg per hectare. It was thought that resistant bacteria mostly passed from livestock to humans via contaminated meat, but the soil, which contains vast numbers of bacteria, may be a more significant route. From the soil, resistant bacteria can get into ground water and from there can be widely spread.

Some outbreaks of human disease have been shown to be caused by pathogens that have evolved drug resistance in an agricultural environment. In 1998, a serious outbreak of *Salmonella* poisoning in Denmark was caused by a drug-resistant strain traced back to a single pig farm. Earlier incidents such as this led to the banning of the use of some antibiotics as growth promoters in livestock in the UK and Europe in the 1970s onwards, but the unrestricted practice still continues in the USA. There is strong evidence that agricultural antibiotic use generates populations of antibiotic-resistant bacteria that contaminate animal-derived food products. These interact with the commensal bacteria in the human gut and speed up the evolution of antibiotic-resistant strains in the human gut flora.

The inappropriate use of antibiotics is not confined to agriculture. There is widespread misuse in the treatment of human disease. In particular, antibiotics are often prescribed for viral illnesses, against which they are ineffective. Even when used, appropriately, against bacterial infections, antibiotics have harmful side-effects. When used inappropriately, as well as being useless, we are left only with their harmful effects.

◯ What adverse effects would you expect antibiotics to have on humans?

⬤ (a) Antibiotics attack the commensal microbes in a body. A common side-effect of antibiotics is diarrhoea, caused by disturbance of the gut flora.

(b) Antibiotics encourage the evolution of antibiotic resistance in commensal bacteria. These are then yet another source of drug-resistant genes for pathogenic bacteria.

Antibacterial agents are increasingly appearing in the homes of entirely healthy people and include household cleaning agents, soaps, detergents, hand lotions and, bizarrely, toothbrushes and chopsticks. Such products feed an obsession for a 'germ-free environment' but they carry considerable risks. Not only do they add to the ubiquity of antimicrobial compounds, favouring the evolution of resistant bacterial strains, they may alter a person's commensal microflora, possibly leading to a greater incidence of allergies in children. Moreover, the normal development of the immune system requires the presence of microbes – host animals raised in a bacteria-free environment have vestigial lymphoid organs.

The genetic changes underlying the evolution of resistance to antimicrobial compounds vary from one pathogen to another. While many pathogens acquire resistant genes by horizontal transfer, resistance in the TB pathogen *Mycobacterium tuberculosis* emerges, within individual hosts, by mutation. This variation has profound implications for the development of strategies to combat drug resistance. For TB, the problem has to be addressed at the level of the individual patient; for other diseases, it is a population-level problem.

The within-host population structure of a pathogen may affect its response to antibiotics. A study of a single patient suffering from multiple liver cysts infected with *E. coli* revealed that long-term treatment with a variety of antibiotics led to the evolution of several drug-resistant *E. coli* strains. As discussed earlier, the body of a host is not a single, homogeneous environment for microbes, but consists of a number of 'habitats', in which microbial evolution can proceed independently.

The evolution of drug resistance has been a major problem in malaria control over many years and has led to the development of a succession of new drugs to replace those that have lost their effectiveness. Resistance of *Plasmodium* species to drugs has evolved at very different rates, depending on the drug and its date of introduction (Figure 2.8).

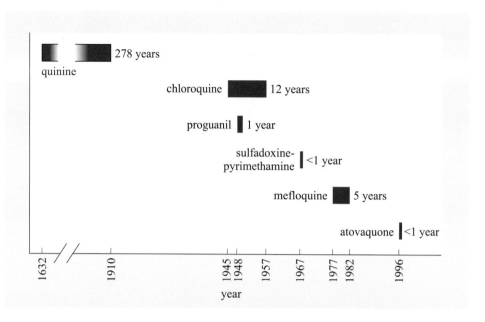

FIGURE 2.8

Variation in the effective life of antimalarial drugs. Purple horizontal bars show, for a succession of drugs, the time from its introduction to the first reports of resistance to that drug. For example, mefloquine was first used in 1977 and resistance to it was first reported in 1982.

For several of these drugs, genetic analyses have identified the alleles that confer resistance in *Plasmodium*. These provide a useful tool for determining the geographic distribution of resistant alleles, so that an appropriate drug can be used in a given area, and for detecting drug resistance in a given area at an early stage.

An interesting question that can be asked in relation to the evolution of drug resistance in pathogens is whether the process can be reversed. Given that drug resistance has evolved by natural selection partly in response to the widespread use of antibiotics, if such use were stopped or greatly reduced, would natural selection reverse the process, and eliminate drug-resistant strains? We would expect it to do so if drug resistance is a costly adaptation for pathogens.

○ Suggest a possible reason for any cost to the pathogen.

● Many drug-resistant genes are encoded in plasmids. Gaining and maintaining a plasmid entails replicating extra DNA. Additionally, if drug resistance involves novel enzymes, their synthesis could be an additional metabolic cost.

This question has been addressed experimentally by making drug-resistant strains of bacteria compete, in cultures or in laboratory animals, with non-resistant strains. If drug resistance incurs a fitness cost, such as a reduced reproduction rate, the non-resistant strains should out-compete the resistant strains. Most of such studies suggest, first, that the costs of resistance are modest and, secondly, that microbes counteract them by acquiring ameliorating adaptations rather than by losing drug resistance. It seems that we cannot look to natural selection to get us out of the mess that we have got ourselves into!

The evolution of drug resistance shows a similar temporal pattern in both clinical and community contexts. Following the introduction of a new antibiotic, the frequency of resistant bacterial strains is low for some time, but then increases rapidly to an equilibrium level at less than 100%. Mathematical models, based on data from actual recent occurrences of drug resistance, suggest the rate of increase is greater and the equilibrium frequency higher when the volume of drug use is higher. Thus, the volume of drug use has a direct effect on the rate of evolution of drug resistance. This suggests that, first, the evolution of drug resistance may be prevented by using drugs conservatively and, secondly, that it can be slowed down if drugs are withdrawn as soon as resistance to them is detected.

Summary of Section 2.6

1   The evolution of antibiotic resistance has been rapid and a major cause for concern in hospital-acquired infections.

2   The scale of antibiotic resistance has been increased by widespread misuse of antibiotics, due to overprescribing, patients not completing their treaments, agricultural applications and use of antibacterial agents in domestic cleaning products.

3   Even when correctly prescribed, antibiotics can generate harmful side-effects due to disruption of the commensal gut flora.

4   Genetic change causing antibiotic resistance may be due to horizontal transfer or mutation.

5   The rate of evolution of drug resistance in *Plasmodium* species has depended on the type of drug. In general, the volume of drug use determines the rate of evolution of resistance.

6   Experimental studies of competition between drug-resistant and wild-type strains indicate that natural selection is unlikely to favour the wild type in an environment free of antibiotics.

Learning outcomes for Chapter 2

When you have studied this chapter, you should be able to:

2.1   Define and use, or recognize definitions and applications of, each of the terms printed in **bold** in the text.

2.2   Describe the three models of coevolution and give examples of two of them. (*Question 2.1*)

2.3   Provide examples of genetic variation in hosts due to coevolution with pathogens and describe genetic variation and its causes in a named pathogen. (*Question 2.2*)

2.4   Provide definitions of virulence and discuss the evidence for the evolution of increasing or decreasing virulence. (*Question 2.1*)

2.5   Discuss mechanisms of host manipulation by pathogens and provide examples for humans and invertebrates. (*Question 2.3*)

2.6   Give examples of the diversity and the threats posed by STIs and discuss the strategies adopted by sexually transmitted pathogens. (*Questions 2.2 and 2.3*)

2.7   Give examples of the diversity of vector-borne diseases, the interactions between pathogen and vector and implications for control of insect vectors. (*Question 2.5*)

2.8   Describe the rates of evolution of antibiotic or drug resistance and discuss reasons for the extent of antibiotic resistance. (*Question 2.4*)

Questions for Chapter 2

Question 2.1

Which of the three models of coevolution predicts a reduction in virulence? Give a short justification for your answer.

Question 2.2

Briefly contrast the importance of sexual reproduction to genetic variation in hosts and pathogens.

Question 2.3

To what extent can STIs be considered as an example of host manipulation by pathogens?

Question 2.4

Based on the information in Section 2.6, write a short set of guidelines for the appropriate use of antibiotics.

Question 2.5

Insects are divided into separate orders, which include flies (Diptera), beetles, (Coleoptera) and butterflies and moths (Lepidoptera). Name the insect order that contains most vectors of human disease. Give one reason why this order of insects has so many vectors.

3 ECOLOGY OF DISEASE

3.1 Patterns of pathogen and host range and abundance

In Chapter 1, we noted that Ecology (and Evolution) extends our consideration of disease from individuals to populations and species. A major set of questions asked by ecologists is how patterns of range (defined below) and abundance of populations of organisms change in time and space. Changes in population abundance in time and space are known as **population dynamics**. Once such patterns are described, we can begin to elucidate the underlying processes that give rise to these patterns. In this section, we will introduce some of the patterns of range and abundance of pathogens and their hosts.

3.1.1 Patterns of range

You have already encountered a variety of **geographical ranges** relevant to infectious disease, defined as the full geographical extent of the organism under consideration; for example, the geographical range of the three major species of *Schistosoma* that cause schistosomiasis (Book 2, Figure 7.7). Whilst it is obvious that the pathogen cannot have a larger range than its host, in fact, in many cases, it has a much smaller range. Contrast the geographical range of the malaria pathogen (Figure 3.1) with the distribution of the human hosts who live in all but the most extreme environments on Earth.

FIGURE 3.1
Changing geographical range of malaria. In 1946, the high risk range was all three coloured areas; by 1966, it was down to the yellow and brown areas; and by 1994 it was only the brown areas.

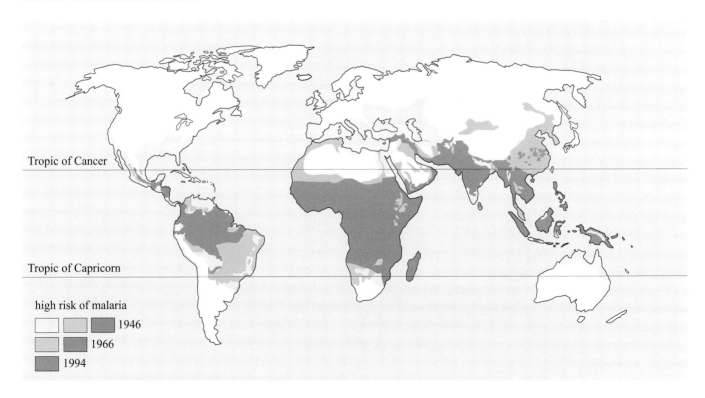

Tropic of Cancer

Tropic of Capricorn

high risk of malaria

| | | | 1946
| | | 1966
| 1994

Not only is the pathogen range much smaller than that of the host, it may also be appreciably smaller than that of the vector. (Recall from the *Malaria* CD-ROM that there are about 70 species of *Anopheles* that can act as vectors.) For example, there are several species of *Anopheles* living in Britain. They share the habitat characteristics of their tropical relatives: one species breeds in brackish waters, one in inland fresh-water and one in water-filled tree holes. The difference in range size between pathogen and vector may not always have been so great. Up until the end of the nineteenth century, there was still indigenous malaria (ague) in the coastal regions of Britain. Thus range areas are themselves dynamic (Figure 3.1).

◯ With reference to Figure 3.1, what are the present-day limits of the range of the pathogens that cause malaria?

⬤ The limits of the pathogen range are roughly between the Tropics of Cancer and Capricorn, i.e. malaria is now primarily a tropical disease with some areas of high risk in northern subtropical areas, e.g. northern India.

◯ How did the range of the malaria pathogens change from 1946 to 1994?

⬤ The range contracted, especially from the northern limits in the southern United States, Mediterranean Europe and parts of the ex-Soviet Union.

This contraction in range has left areas of the world with the nuisance of biting mosquitoes or related flies, but no longer the threat of malaria (such as in the coastal regions of Britain).

3.1.2 Patterns of abundance

It should be apparent to you already that assessing pathogen abundance is extremely difficult. Book 1 introduced a variety of measures of disease abundance that are developed further in Book 6.

◯ Are measures of abundance of cases of disease, such as prevalence or incidence, also measures of pathogen abundance?

⬤ Indirectly, as they are measures of the number of human hosts affected by a particular pathogen.

Numbers of infected human hosts may be closely correlated with abundance of pathogens. But they may also be grossly misleading, for example, if the numbers of pathogens per human host are highly variable, or if many pathogens live outside the human host, e.g. in the external environment, in vectors or in intermediate hosts.

Consider the problem of variation of pathogen abundance in the host. A useful way of expressing the abundance of the pathogen is with respect to its relative abundance in different host individuals, in other words, its distribution amongst the host individuals. This is especially useful for larger pathogens, where the number of individual pathogens per host shows a characteristic pattern (Figure 3.2).

◯ How is the abundance per host represented in Figure 3.2?

⬤ As the worm burden, i.e. the number of worms per host.

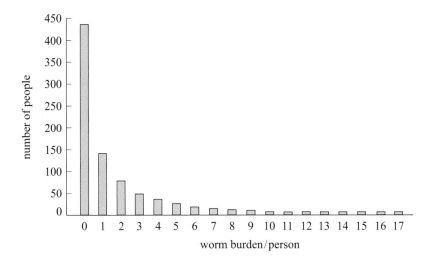

FIGURE 3.2 The frequency distribution of the human roundworm (*Ascaris lumbricoides*) in a rural population in Korea.

○ From the data presented in Figure 3.2, what conclusion can you draw about the distribution of *Ascaris lumbricoides* in the host population?

● The majority of the host population is uninfected by the pathogen whilst a few hosts carry the majority of the worms.

We have already seen an example of this distribution in Book 2 with reference to hookworms (p. 134), showing that a few individuals carry a heavy worm burden, whilst many individuals have no or very few worms.

○ Recall from Book 2 the name given to this type of distribution amongst hosts.

● This kind of distribution pattern is referred to as a clumped or overdispersed distribution. It is also referred to as an aggregated distribution. All three names refer to the large number of pathogens in a small number of hosts.

The **aggregated distribution** or pattern of relative abundance is one of three types of pattern met in ecological (and other biological) studies (Box 3.1). If we were to consider the patterns of malaria pathogen abundance, then, as with the geographical range, we would also need to consider the abundance of the pathogen in the vector. Indeed, for a full appreciation of the abundance of pathogens, we need to consider patterns of abundance within the host, within intermediate hosts or vectors and, in some cases, the abiotic (non-living) environment. Fortunately, understanding the dynamics of disease does not usually depend on a complete assessment of pathogen abundance. This will be illustrated in Section 3.2 and in Book 6.

BOX 3.1 Regular, random and aggregated patterns of abundance

Organisms can be distributed in various ways in space. This may include the distribution (pattern of abundance) of organisms in different habitats or different parts of the same habitat. With pathogens, we consider the patterns of abundance amongst hosts (see main text). In other branches of biology we might consider, for example, the patterns of abundance of cells on a microscope slide. Three common patterns of abundance are random, regular and aggregated. These patterns can be visualized in two ways. First, as the distribution of organisms (such as pathogens) in a grid of habitat patches (such as host organisms), and secondly, as a histogram of the frequency of habitat patches or hosts occupied by different numbers of organisms (e.g. Figure 3.2).

A regular pattern is characterized by an equal number of pathogens in each host. In an aggregated pattern, there is a relatively high frequency of hosts with few pathogens and a low frequency of hosts with a high number of pathogens (see example in main text). In this case, the mean number of pathogens per host is not helpful in describing the abundance of a pathogen. A random pattern lies somewhere between regular and aggregated.

An important distinction here is between the aggregation of the pathogen in the host and the distribution (and possible aggregation) of the host. The latter can be described in the same way as aggregation of pathogens (Box 3.1) except that now the grid is composed of units of geographical space amongst which the humans (or other hosts) are divided. This means that some areas may have a much higher human **population density** than other areas. Population density, defined as numbers per unit area or, in the case of pathogens, numbers per host, is an important variable in population dynamics. Humans are often highly aggregated in space, especially in developing countries (Figure 3.3). A feature of some of the major historical and contemporary diseases, such as plague, cholera, HIV and TB, is their high prevalence amongst aggregated host populations due to enhanced rates of transmission.

FIGURE 3.3
An example of aggregated pattern of abundance of human hosts in space.

We will now move on to consider some of the *processes* giving rise to these observed patterns of range and abundance.

Summary of Section 3.1

1 Changes in population abundance in time and space are referred to as population dynamics. Geographical ranges, comprising the full range of a species, are also dynamic.

2 The geographical range of the malaria pathogens, has declined in the last century and is now largely confined to tropical regions.

3 Prevalence of disease may be a misleading description of pathogen abundance. Similarly, mean pathogen abundance may be unhelpful in describing the distribution of pathogens amongst hosts. Aggregated distributions of pathogens (especially larger species) are well known.

4 Hosts may also be aggregated in space, with the resulting high population densities favouring the transmission of certain pathogens.

3.2 Population dynamics of host and pathogen: an example of a compartmental model

The previous section on patterns of abundance introduced us to the idea that we can identify a series of places (including various categories of host) in which the pathogen can exist (and various places where they do *not* exist). We will refer to these places as **compartments**. At a particular point in time, individual hosts can be categorized into one of four compartments, which were introduced in Book 1 and Chapter 1 of this book:

- susceptible – not yet infected by the pathogen;

- infected but latent (i.e. non-infectious);

- infectious;

- recovered and immune.

(It may also be that individuals do not become immune or they do not recover.)

An individual host can pass through all four stages, i.e. at different times the host may contribute to each of the four compartments, or can die from the disease. The duration of the second and third stages is determined by the latent and infectious periods characteristic of the disease (see Chapter 1).

If we can determine the abundance of the hosts representing each of the compartments at one point in time and the rate at which the hosts flow between compartments, then we can begin to model the population dynamics of the pathogen and host (models of human diseases were introduced in Chapter 1 – the concept of mathematical modelling and the rationale for modelling is discussed in Book 6, Section 2). These models help us to understand why some pathogens spread rapidly through a host population whilst others remain at more or less similar values or decline. Such knowledge will be extremely useful when we come to consider ways of combating a disease.

So let us start building a compartmental model using the example of malaria and following the categories of host identified above. We have purposely chosen a complex example in order to illustrate the ecological and biological issues. However, it is an example with which you are (hopefully!) familiar from the CD-ROM introduced in Book 1. This example immediately creates a new level of complexity as we have a human host and an insect vector giving rise to eight compartments (Table 3.1).

TABLE 3.1 Organization of compartments for a model of the dynamics of malaria.

Category	Human host compartment	Insect vector
pathogen-free (susceptible)	a	b
pathogen-infected (latent)	c	d
pathogen-infected (infectious)	e	f
recovered	g	h
total	a+c+e+g hosts	b+d+f+h insect vectors

We will use this compartmental model to explore the dynamics of the malaria host–vector–pathogen interaction, i.e. how numbers in the different compartments change over time. For example, we might ask, under what conditions and how rapidly would a malaria infection spread through a human population? Let us attempt to answer this question using the compartmental model. Imagine the scenario of an isolated village with resident populations of 99 humans and 1000 female mosquitoes who are all free of *Plasmodium* infection. We will assume that humans of different age and gender are equally likely to be infected with the malaria parasite (we will need to make many such, potentially unrealistic, assumptions). We will also assume that the mosquito population is more or less constant regardless of the presence of malaria; in fact, we will assume there are always 1000 female mosquitoes in the village. Now imagine that a single recently infected human enters the village. We will designate as the beginning of day 1 the point in time that the recently arrived human becomes infectious (and before he or she is bitten by a village mosquito). The values in the compartments for start of day 1 are given in Table 3.2.

TABLE 3.2 Start of day 1: newly arrived human becomes infectious.

Category	Human host compartment	Insect vector (females)
pathogen-free (susceptible)	99	1000
pathogen-infected (latent)	0	0
pathogen-infected (infectious)	1	0
recovered	0	0
total	100	1000

We will need to gather some more data and make a few more assumptions before we proceed. It is valuable to list these in order to see how far our model might depart from reality and to note the variability that is inherent in the malaria host–vector–pathogen system.

Assumptions

- no previous history of malaria in village;

- all hosts are equally susceptible;

- there are always about 1000 female mosquitoes in the village;

- infected human arriving at the beginning of the infectious period.

Data required to proceed with the dynamic compartmental model include:

- length of life and survival of mosquito;

- number of people bitten per day;

- duration of components of life cycle of the pathogen.

The required data are highly variable and depend on the species of pathogen and mosquito and the geographical location under consideration. However, epidemiologists have gathered a lot of related data that may be useful. Let us attempt to tease these data out from the epidemiological data on the *Malaria* CD (you do not have to refer to the CD here, but you may wish to follow up some of the details below).

How long does the mosquito live?

Female mosquitoes have a daily mortality rate of between 5 to 25%. In other words, somewhere between 95% (0.95) and 75% (0.75) of female mosquitoes survive until the next day. This means that if we start with 1000, there will be somewhere between $1000 \times 0.95 = 950$ and $1000 \times 0.75 = 750$ remaining after one day (this ignores recruitment of new mosquitoes – you will see the reason for this later).

▢ What is the maximum and minimum number after two days?

▣ Maximum after two days = $950 \times 0.95 = 902.5$ or $1000 \times 0.95 \times 0.95$
Minimum after two days = $750 \times 0.75 = 562.5$ or $1000 \times 0.75 \times 0.75$.

This can be expressed as a simple equation to give the number of mosquitoes alive after n days, given an initial number of mosquitoes:

> no. of mosquitoes alive after n days = initial no. of mosquitoes $\times$
> (fraction surviving)^n (Eqn 3.1)

▢ Using Equation 3.1, what would be the number alive after 3 days if the daily survival rate was 0.9 and the initial number was 1000?

▣ Number alive after 3 days = $1000 \times (0.9)^3 = 1000 \times 0.729 = 729$.

These values can be incorporated into the dynamic compartmental model. After every day, we can multiply the number of mosquitoes by the survival rate. We will need to do this because we want to track the abundance of the infected mosquitoes. Appropriate values of daily survival rate will be chosen below.

How many people are bitten per day?

Female mosquitoes mostly feed every 2 to 4 days. We also have to take into account the preferences for humans. *Anopheles gambiae* feeds on average once every two nights and prefers feeding on humans whereas *Anopheles culicifacies* feeds once every three nights but feeds predominantly (about 80% of the time) on cattle with only about 20% of feeds on humans. This information can be used to calculate a **daily bite rate** of humans by female mosquitoes.

○ For these two species, what is the (average) daily bite rate on humans?

● *Anopheles gambiae*: 0.5 (assuming 100% feeding on humans)
Anopheles culicifacies: 0.33 × 0.2 (20% preference for humans) = 0.066.

In our compartmental model, we will work with an average daily bite rate of 0.2, i.e. somewhere between the rates for *A. gambiae* and *A. culicifacies*.

Duration of components of life cycle of pathogen

This information is needed in order to determine the length of the latent and infectious periods in both the human and the insect vector. Not all of this is directly accessible from the *Malaria* CD-ROM. The following information is taken from the CD-ROM and other sources and refers to *Plasmodium falciparum* unless stated otherwise.

Gametogenesis of *P. falciparum* in the mosquito takes about 18–24 hours and sporogony is about 9–10 days (Figure 3.4, stages E and F), longer for other *Plasmodium* species. Thus, it is reasonable to assume that the minimum time for a mosquito to become infective after biting an infected human and itself becoming infected is about 11 days. This is the duration of the latent period in the mosquito. Sporozoites can remain in the mosquito salivary gland(s) for up to 59 days. This means that once a mosquito has become infective it is highly likely to remain infective until it dies.

○ Why is the mosquito *highly likely* to remain infective until it dies?

● Because even with a high daily survival rate of 0.9, the probability of being alive after 59 days is $0.9^{59} = 0.002$, i.e. a very small number.

In humans, passage of the sporozoites through the blood system to the liver (stage A, Figure 3.4) is quite rapid. After 45 minutes, most sporozoites will have left the blood. Hypnozoites usually remain in the liver from 9 to 16 days (stage B) – although some may remain there much longer. The time from schizont to gametocyte is about 48 hours and gametogenesis takes between 10 to 12 days. The minimum duration of the latent period in humans is therefore about $9 + 2 + 10 = 21$ days. We will assume for convenience a latent period in humans of 22 days (i.e. twice the latent period in the mosquito). The delays that occur in the liver mean that humans may remain infective for many weeks following the latent period. There may also be dormancy and reactivation of the pathogen (see Section 3.3).

Now we return to the compartment model and see what happens after the point in time when the infected human became infectious. After one day, we expect that each female mosquito will have bitten 0.2 humans (on average!). Therefore, a total of $1000 × 0.2 = 200$ humans will have been bitten. As there are only 100 humans, this means that every human is bitten twice each day by different mosquitoes. This bite rate will remain constant as long as there is no change in the number of

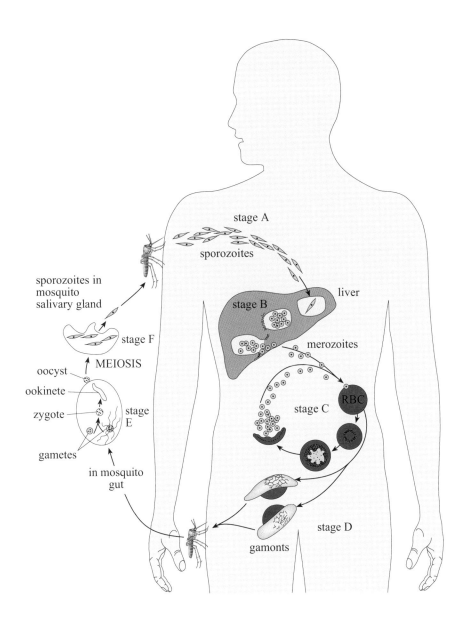

stage A

sporozoites

sporozoites in
mosquito
salivary gland

liver

stage B

stage F

merozoites

MEIOSIS

oocyst

ookinete

zygote

stage
E

RBC

stage C

gametes

in mosquito
gut

stage D

gamonts

FIGURE 3.4
Plasmodium falciparum life cycle.
The durations of stages are given in
the text.

humans and female mosquitoes (and the assumptions of the model hold). As one of
the humans is infective, at the end of one day, two of the mosquitoes have become
infected (assuming that the bite results in successful transfer of the pathogen). So
at the end of day 1 we have the situation in Table 3.3.

TABLE 3.3 Compartmental model at the end of day 1.

Category	Human host compartment	Insect vector (females)
pathogen-free (susceptible)	99	998
pathogen-infected (latent)	0	2
pathogen-infected (infectious)	1	0
recovered	0	0
total	100	1000

At the end of day 2, two more mosquitoes have become infectious. Assume that the infected human remains infectious in the village for two days (for simplicity assume that the infectious human leaves the village after two days). There will now be four infected mosquitoes. Now, let us move on to the end of day 11. We can estimate the number of infected mosquitoes alive after 11 days using Equation 3.1:

$$\text{no. of infected mosquitoes after 11 days} = 2 \times (0.9)^{11} = 2 \times 0.314 = 0.628.$$

We also have the two mosquitoes that were infected on day 2. The number of these alive at the end of day 11 is $2 \times (0.9)^{10} = 0.697$. Note that we are also assuming that the females that became infected were newly emerged individuals. These data are now entered into the compartmental model (Table 3.4).

TABLE 3.4 Compartmental model after 11 days.

Category	Human host compartment	Insect vector
pathogen-free (susceptible)	99	$1000 - 1.325$[†]
pathogen-infected (latent)	0	$0.628 + 0.697 = 1.325$
pathogen-infected (infectious)	0	0
left village*	1	n/a
total	100	1000

*Note that the recovered category has been replaced by an emigration category – we have assumed that the infected human left the village after two days.

[†]Recall the assumption that the female mosquito population stays at 1000. In fact, the number of susceptible mosquitoes will not affect the model (as long as the number is large).

At this point, you may be wondering about the legitimacy of using fractions of mosquitoes and fractions of humans! For a general mathematical model, this is not a problem. The interpretation in these cases can be the probability that a mosquito or human is alive as opposed to the actual number of mosquitoes or humans. It can then be applied to a problem with, e.g., 10 000 or 100 000 humans. We have to be more careful with specific models that are applied to real populations of a certain size, especially where the number of individuals is small.

On day 12, we move into a new dynamic phase in which the first infected mosquitoes become infectious. For simplicity, let us treat the mosquitoes infected on day 1 and day 2 as becoming infectious on the same day and that they have the abundance calculated at the end of 11 days. The number of humans bitten by the infectious mosquitoes on day 12 is therefore 1.325×0.2 (bite rate) $= 0.265$ (Table 3.5).

TABLE 3.5 Compartmental model on day 12.

Category	Human host compartment	Insect vector
pathogen-free (susceptible)	$99 - 0.265 = 98.735$	$1000 - 1.325$
pathogen-infected (latent)	0.265	0
pathogen-infected (infectious)	0	1.325
left village	1	n/a
total	100	1000

As the mathematics rapidly becomes complicated, we need to make some simplifying assumptions that will allow us to continue making predictions about the population dynamics without qualitatively affecting the model. One simplifying assumption is that the infectious mosquitoes only bite over two days (days 12 and 13). (This may be an overestimate, as any one mosquito only needs to feed every two to four days. On the other hand, an infected mosquito only transfers about 10% of its sporozoites in one bite.) Therefore, we need to calculate the number of humans bitten by the infectious mosquitoes on day 13:

no. of day 1 infectious mosquitoes surviving $= 2 \times 0.9^{12} = 2 \times 0.282 = 0.564$

no. of day 2 infectious mosquitoes surviving $= 2 \times 0.9^{11} = 2 \times 0.314 = 0.628$

total no. of infectious mosquitoes on day 13 $= 1.192$.

The number of humans bitten by infectious mosquitoes on day 13 is therefore 1.192×0.2 (bite rate) $= 0.238$ (Table 3.6), giving a total of 0.503 infected humans.

TABLE 3.6 Compartmental model on day 13.

Category	Human host compartment	Insect vector
pathogen-free (susceptible)	$99 - 0.503 = 98.497$	$1000 - 1.192$
pathogen-infected (latent)	$0.265 + 0.238 = 0.503$	0
pathogen-infected (infectious)	0	1.192
left village	1	n/a
total	100	1000

After day 13, we are assuming that the infectious mosquitoes have died. So on day 14 we have the situation in Table 3.7.

TABLE 3.7 Compartmental model on day 14.

Category	Human host compartment	Insect vector
pathogen-free (susceptible)	98.497	1000
pathogen-infected (latent)	0.503	0
pathogen-infected (infectious)	0	0
left village	1	n/a
total	100	1000

○ How long will the compartment values remain the same as day 14?

● Until the first newly infected human becomes infectious, which is 22 days after first being bitten by an infectious mosquito. This occurred on day 12 so the first newly infected human becomes infectious on day 34.

Let us assume that humans infected on days 12 and 13 become infectious on day 34. Day 34 will be like day 1 when the infectious human arrived in the village. On day 1, there was one infectious human who got bitten by two mosquitoes. The difference on day 34 is that there are 0.503 humans who are infectious (Table 3.8).

TABLE 3.8 Compartmental model on day 34.

Category	Human host compartment	Insect vector
pathogen-free (susceptible)	98.497	1000
pathogen-infected (latent)	0	0
pathogen-infected (infectious)	0.503	0
left village	1	0
total	100	1000

○ Contrasting Table 3.8 with Table 3.2, what do you predict will happen to the pathogen?

● The pathogen population is not likely to be sustained in the village because 0.503 is less than 1.

We have reached an important conclusion about the dynamics of the pathogen. Under this scenario, the pathogen population is predicted not to persist in the host population (the village). Indeed, we would predict that it would eventually go extinct.

So, under what conditions might the pathogen population increase? A useful quantity to calculate would be the minimum requirements for one or more infectious persons on day 34. To do this we have to look at each of the variables to see which, if any, might naturally alter and therefore can be changed in the model to favour increase in the pathogen population. This will be a useful exercise when we come to think of ways of controlling malaria (as opposed to looking at ways in which it might increase!).

○ Suggest two ways in which the abundance of the pathogen might be increased in the village following infection.

● An increase in the daily bite rate and an increase in the number of times the first infected person is bitten (by higher bite rate and/or by longer exposure before isolation or leaving the village).

We have not considered pathogen life cycle, which is already at minimum duration, and mosquito survival, which is already high. Let us take the daily bite rate (b) as the variable to investigate. In order to determine the requirement for a minimum of one infectious person on day 34, we need to solve the following equation:

1 infectious person on day 34 = (no. of infectious mosquitoes surviving from day 1 to 12 (1.325, see Table 3.5) × bite rate, b) + (no. of infectious mosquitoes surviving from day 2 to 12 (1.192, see Table 3.6) × bite rate, b).

This can be written as an algebraic equation (see Book 6, Box 3.2 if you need help in manipulating equations):

$$1 = (1.325b) + (1.192b)$$

$$1 = 2.517b$$

$$b = 1/2.517$$

$$b = 0.397$$

For convenience let us take b as 0.4.

(Note that if the mosquitoes only bite once, then we have $1 = 1.325b$, i.e. b is 0.75.)

☐ Is this value of bite rate (0.4) unrealistically high?

⬤ No, it is less than that recorded for *Anopheles gambiae* (0.5).

If b is greater than 0.4, then the pathogen population will increase in the host population. If b is less than 0.4, the pathogen population will decline. The daily bite rate value of 0.4 is therefore a threshold for persistence of the pathogen.

So, if all the other variables of the model are held at the assumed values (and the general assumptions of the model hold), daily bite rate represents an important controlling variable on the success of the pathogen.

☐ Considering the potential control of the disease, how could daily bite rate be decreased below the critical value of 0.4?

⬤ One straightforward method is to use nets over beds or hammocks, coinciding use with the peak biting times (early evening). Use of mosquito repellents can also dramatically reduce the frequency of bites.

Development of this model has been helpful in showing the difficulties of working with complex host–pathogen systems and the potential predictive power of mathematical models of disease (see Box 3.2). This is especially important for a disease that continues to kill at least one million people per year. The modelling is further justified on two grounds. First, the role of mosquitoes (and daily bite rate) in a number of globally important diseases in addition to malaria (such as dengue, Figure 3.5, yellow fever and filariasis – see earlier discussion in the course, e.g.

BOX 3.2   Sir Ronald Ross and the history of mathematical models of malaria transmission

Construction of mathematical models to understand the dynamics of malaria first began in the early 20th century with the pioneering work of Sir Ronald Ross (1857–1932). In the late 1890s, he had demonstrated the life cycle of the malarial parasites in mosquitoes, thereby confirming the role of the vectors in the disease. Ross dedicated much of his subsequent working life to understanding ways to control malaria. He undertook field work in many parts of the world including the Middle East and West Africa and developed mathematical models of malaria epidemiology, published in a series of works from 1906 to 1916. He not only sustained a wider interest in mathematics but also received critical acclaim for his poetry! Ross's contribution was recognized in a series of awards, including the Nobel Prize, and many aspects of modern epidemiological models of malaria transmission have their roots in his work. The *Malaria* CD-ROM gives examples of epidemiological models (e.g. Screens 30 and 34 of the 'Epidemiology' tutorial). You are not expected to study these, but you may find them interesting, especially after studying Book 6, as the 'professional' version of the model described in this chapter.

FIGURE 3.5
A dengue mosquito biting.

Section 2.5 of this book and Book 2, Section 7.5.2). Secondly, the concept of pathogen populations increasing or decreasing in host populations is developed and generalized to all diseases in Book 6 (in particular with regard to the important variable R_0, pronounced 'are nought') and it is not discussed further in this book.

This discussion of conditions under which the pathogen population will increase or decrease is an example of wider ecological debate about the nature of stability of population dynamics and conditions for extinction and colonization. In the malaria case, we have a situation analogous to a ball balancing on a very fine point (Figure 3.6a).

It is mathematically possible for the ball to stay on the peak. But if there is even the slightest change in conditions (e.g. as represented in the malaria example above by alterations in daily bite rate), it will roll one way or the other. Thus, it is possible to have a population persisting with one infected host, but it requires all the variables to stay at the same value over a long period of time. This is highly unlikely! Much more likely is the situation in which the pathogen population increases or decreases. This then raises new questions. Will the decline in the pathogen be continued, ultimately resulting in its local extinction? Will the increase in the pathogen population continue until all susceptible hosts have been infected? It is likely that neither of these will occur. Instead, we may have either a high increase followed by (possibly dramatic) reductions in population size (Figure 3.6b) or reductions to a few infected hosts. Over longer periods of time, this may be seen as cycles of pathogen population abundance or at least fluctuations in pathogen population size. This is the subject of the next section.

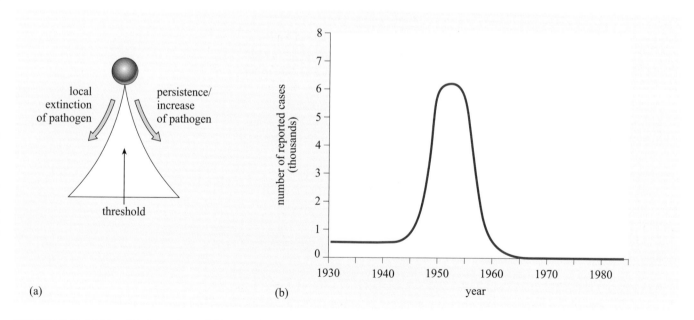

(a)

(b)

FIGURE 3.6 (a) Unstable dynamics and (b) example of an epidemic (polio, detailed in the *Polio* Case Study).

Summary of Section 3.2

1 A compartmental model is constructed to investigate the possible spread of malaria through a village. Four compartments of host and vector are recognized: susceptible, infected but latent, infectious and recovered.

2 The assumptions of the model include equal susceptibility of the hosts, a constant high vector population and the introduction of the pathogen by a single infected host.

3 Data on mosquito survival and longevity, daily bite rate and duration of the stages of the pathogen life cycle are sourced from the *Malaria* CD-ROM and other sources.

4 Changes in the numbers of hosts and vectors in the different compartments are calculated over a total of 34 days. In this example, comparison of the number of infected persons on day 34 with the number on day 1 (one person) show whether the pathogen will increase or decrease in the village.

5 Based on the assumptions of this model, a daily bite rate of 0.4 is required for persistence of the pathogen. This value is identified as a threshold for persistence.

3.3 Further examples of host–pathogen dynamics: cycles and fluctuations in abundance

Why might some diseases show cycles or predictable fluctuations in abundance? These fluctuations may be linked to seasons, e.g. the higher incidence of influenza in winter (Book 1, Figure 2.7, see further examples in Book 6, Section 5) or the onset of yellow fever with the rainy season, due to the hatching of eggs of previously infected mosquitoes. In these cases, there are clear reasons why the pathogen population should change in abundance – survival, fecundity and/or transmission of the pathogens can all be affected by the environmental conditions. Another more contentious example is the outbreaks of *Vibrio cholerae* infection which appear to be associated with climatic cycles and ocean plankton blooms (see the *Cholera* Case Study).

☐ With reference to Book 3, what else might be affected by the environmental conditions for a given pathogen species?

▓ Defence of the host may be impaired (e.g. immunodeficiency, Book 3, p. 102).

These explanations of pathogen abundance driven by external environmental patterns, such as weather, are examples of factors **extrinsic** to the host–pathogen system. The same factors may have been responsible for shifts in the range of the pathogens over time.

In some cases, there appear to be no obvious extrinsic factors. In these examples, cycles or predictable fluctuations of outbreak years may occur over tens of years. A set of data on epidemics recorded in the United States from 1657 to 1918 by present-day genealogists is given in Figure 3.7.

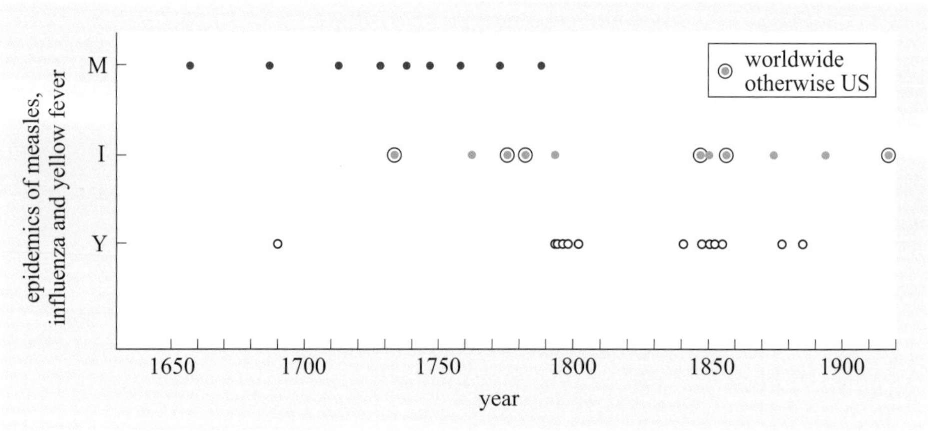

FIGURE 3.7
Epidemics of measles (M, red),
influenza (I, green) and yellow fever
(Y, black) from 1657 to 1918 recorded
by genealogists.

◯ How reliable are these data? (*Hint*: think back to Book 4.)

● They depend on correct diagnosis at the time – this may be incorrect for
influenza and possibly yellow fever (which may have been confused with
hepatitis). They are also not a systematic sample – there is not a standard
definition of an epidemic and they have not been taken from a fixed number of
people in a standardized manner. (See Book 4 for discussion of notifiable
diseases (p. 11) and Book 6 for examples of sampling epidemiological data.)

However, these data are indicative of the likely frequency of major outbreaks of
given diseases. Note that they are not records of pathogen abundance but
indications of disease prevalence. More reliable sets of data are provided in the
returns of general practitioners and other health workers from the mid-twentieth
century to the present day (see Book 6 for details).

◯ What conclusions can be reached about the frequency of occurrence of the
epidemics of the three diseases listed in Figure 3.7?

● Some of the yellow fever epidemics are widely spaced, whilst others appear to
be tightly clustered. There is no obvious pattern with the influenza epidemics.
The measles epidemics may be increasing in frequency. Indeed, we can contrast
this frequency of occurrence of these measles epidemics every ten years or
more with those every two years in England and Wales from 1948 to 1982 (see
Book 6, Figure 5.1).

As you will see in Book 6, the analysis of measles data has been particularly fruitful
for its insights into cycles of pathogen abundance. For example, Grenfell and co-
workers have used weekly statistics on measles data from 1944 to 1994 in England
and Wales to illustrate waves of infection originating in large cities and then
spreading to surrounding towns and villages. This gives the cycles of abundance a
spatial dimension, i.e. the peaks of abundance are not restricted to one particular
locality but are able to spread between localities. It may be that there are some
correlations of the outbreaks with climate patterns, but this is not always the case.

Where there are no apparent extrinsic events driving the dynamics, we need to
consider what **intrinsic** processes might be driving the dynamics of the pathogen
and host, i.e. processes derived from the interaction between host and pathogen.
We will consider a little later some details of these intrinsic processes. The search

FIGURE 3.8
Lynx chasing a snowshoe hare.

for intrinsic mechanisms that generate cycles in abundance is an issue that has fascinated ecologists for many years. It is a phenomenon that stretches far beyond host-pathogen interactions. Cycles of abundance can be found in organisms as diverse as lynx, herbivorous insects and grouse (Figures 3.8 and 3.9).

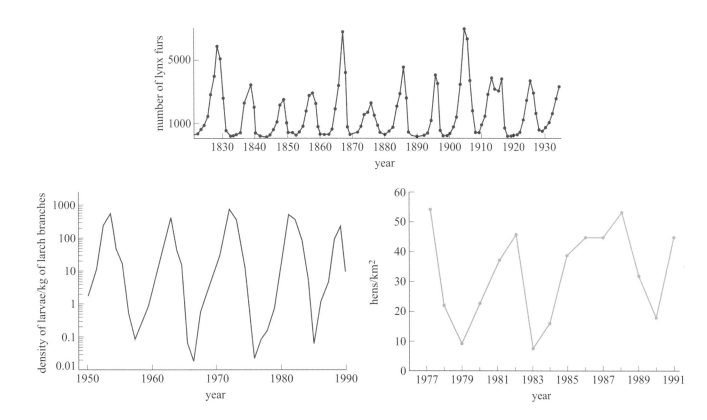

FIGURE 3.9 Cycles of abundance in (a) lynx (based on trap returns), (b) larch bud moth and (c) grouse (mature females).

What do the ecological systems in Figure 3.9 have in common with the host–pathogen system? First, they all involve (+/−) interactions as described in Chapter 1. But that is not unusual; many species are involved in such interactions. A second important property is that all the predators/pathogens/herbivores (i.e. those species that gain from the interaction) *specialize* on a small number of host or prey species. Indeed, they usually specialize on just one species. For example, lynx (where they show cycles in abundance) feed predominantly on snowshoe hare (Figure 3.8), and the larch bud moth (*Zeiraphera diniana*) feeds only on larch (*Larix decidua*). Grouse specialize on heather (*Calluna*) species, but in their case it is probably a parasitic nematode that specializes on them which is important. You encountered this parasite in Chapter 1 (Table 1.2). In the early 1990s, Dobson and Hudson used a combination of experiments and mathematical models to show that cycles of abundance in grouse could be due to the grouse's interaction with a parasitic nematode.

A consequence of this specificity is that changes in the abundance of one species are expected to lead to changes in the abundance of the other. To illustrate this, let us imagine a system of one predator and one prey species (the lynx and the hare). In this simple scenario, lynx only eat hares and hares only eat grass. Assume that grass is abundant and unaffected by the numbers of hare.

○ What do you predict would be the effect of an increase in the number of lynx?

● They would eat more hares and the number of hares would fall.

○ What would be the effect on the lynx of this reduction in the number of hares?

● The lynx would have less to eat and therefore their survival and/or fecundity would decline.

○ What would be the effect of reducing survival and/or fecundity of the lynx?

● They would reduce in abundance.

○ What would be the effect of reducing numbers of lynx?

● Hares would increase in abundance!

You will see from this set of questions and responses that it is easy to generate an intuitive argument (the real situation is inevitably more complex than this!) to explain why lynx and hare would cycle in abundance. This is particularly true if there is a **delay** in response of one species to changes in abundance of the other. For example, whilst reduced numbers of hares this year may result in reduced fecundity of lynx in the same year, this is not manifested as change in the abundance of mature lynx until several years later.

Very similar arguments were applied by Dobson and Hudson to the grouse–parasite system. They showed that birds treated with chemicals to kill the parasites had higher adult survival and higher hatching success. Furthermore, they showed that there were significant *delays* in the parasite life cycle, caused by the ability of the larval parasites to arrest their development after infecting a host. The authors' detailed mathematical studies demonstrated that cycles of abundance with a period of 8 or 10 years could be produced by a particular combination of larval arrestment duration (typically 2–4 months) and host birth rate.

Delays in the pathogen life cycle are found widely, including in human pathogens. They occur due to the duration of development and reproduction of the pathogen in the host (i.e. the latent period) and due to dormant periods, e.g. between the stages of syphilis. Dormancy also appears to be an important feature of prion and virus life cycles. What might be the adaptive explanation for long periods of dormancy? Clues come from comparison with other ecological systems where dormancy is a feature. Two examples of such ecological dormancy come to mind. The first is amongst annual plants, the seeds of which may remain dormant in the soil for many years, i.e. for periods of time which far exceed the generation time of the organism. The second example is the dormancy of cicadas (Figure 3.10; a type of plant-feeding insect whose loud noise in late afternoon and early evening is well known to anyone who has travelled in tropical and subtropical regions). These two examples represent two different reasons for dormancy. In the first, the benefit of dormancy is that the seeds of many annual plants are only able to germinate under certain conditions such as following physical disturbance, flooding or intermittent rains. These events may be infrequent and unpredictable in occurrence, e.g. in desert environments. Hence there is a selective advantage to plants that can persist during unfavourable conditions in the dormant state (which usually acts to protect them against the adverse environmental conditions) and respond quickly to intermittent favourable conditions.

FIGURE 3.10 A cicada.

In the second example, selection has favoured cicadas that emerge infrequently and thereby avoid predation. This is further supported by the emergence times of cicadas, for example every 13 or 17 years in Indiana in the United States.

○ Why is emergence every 13 or 17 years favourable to a potential prey species?

● Because 13 and 17 are prime numbers and cover a protracted period of time, which means that predators can only specialize on these prey by emerging at exactly the same time and with the same period. Predators that emerge with any other time period (or show peaks, e.g. every five or ten years) would rarely coincide with the peaks of prey abundance and therefore be unable to specialize on the prey.

Do either of these explanations for dormancy in non-pathogen species help with interpretation of patterns of dormancy in pathogen species? It is possible that both are relevant. The first explanation may be appropriate to pathogens that have specialized requirements within the host, e.g. contact with a limited set of cell types, or require the host to be at a particular developmental state, but have a broad type of transmission or unspecialized movements within the host. Thus, the pathogen cannot guarantee when and where it enters the host and needs to enter a dormant state before it encounters a part of the host in a receptive or suitable condition. Dormancy in malaria may be related to its exit strategy from the host. Hypnozoites of *Plasmodium vivax* and *P. ovule* in the liver can be reactivated up to 18 months later; this may be seasonal and coincide with reappearance of the vector (*Malaria* CD).

The second explanation may also be correct. The pathogen is seeking to evade the host's defences and may be aided by long periods of dormancy during which it remains undetectable by the host's defence. This links back to the examples of pathogens transmitted by direct contact that may spend many years inside the host (Table 1.4).

Given the presence of these delays, can the population dynamics argument applied to grouse and their parasites be applied to humans and their pathogens? Certainly we know that humans have host-specific pathogens, that those pathogens can have an effect on survival and fecundity and that those pathogens can have periods of dormancy in the host. A major difference from the grouse system is that humans have a much longer generation time and effects on human fecundity are not going to respond numerically in the manner of the grouse. In other words, humans cannot show great variation in 'hatching' success! Another problem is that humans may be interacting with a much wider array of pathogens than the grouse, or perhaps more accurately, that there is no one pathogen for humans that is of such overwhelming importance as the parasitic nematode is to the grouse (99% of juvenile birds in a sample of 2723 were infected). If there were situations in which humans were mainly interacting with one pathogen whose impact on human populations was high in terms of survival and/or fecundity (TB in pre-industrial England may have been a candidate), then we might expect to see cycles of host abundance. But such dynamics might be played out over tens or hundreds of years and therefore possibly be undetectable on the time-scales of scientific studies. With humans, the most interesting host–pathogen population dynamics are probably happening at the cellular level within a single individual, where the immune system is interacting with an array of pathogens. It is the cellular level to which we now direct our attention.

Summary of Section 3.3

1   Fluctuations or cycles of abundance of pathogens could be due to extrinsic causes, e.g. seasonal weather patterns.

2   Evidence from historical and current data point to diseases with a variety of time periods of outbreaks or epidemics.

3   Intrinsic processes underlying cycles in abundance in ecological systems have been linked to host specialization and delays in response of one population to changes in the other. These processes are illustrated by the interaction between grouse and its major parasitic nematode.

4   Delays in host–pathogen systems appear to be widespread, with pathogens benefiting by, e.g. avoiding the host defence and timing completion of the life cycle in the host with vector activity.

5   Cycles in abundance of human pathogens may be rare due to the variety of human pathogens, the long generation time of humans and the lack of numerical responses in fecundity. If they do occur, such cycles might be undetectable over the normal time-scales of scientific study.

3.4 Population dynamics of pathogens in the host

At several points in this chapter and in other parts of the course, we have discussed the potentially high rates of population increase of different pathogens. In this section, we will quantify some of these rates and discuss their implications for survival of the pathogen in the host. Note that in this section we focus on population dynamics *within* the host – the parallel story of spread of disease between hosts, drawing on similar methods, is given in Book 6, Section 1.2.1.

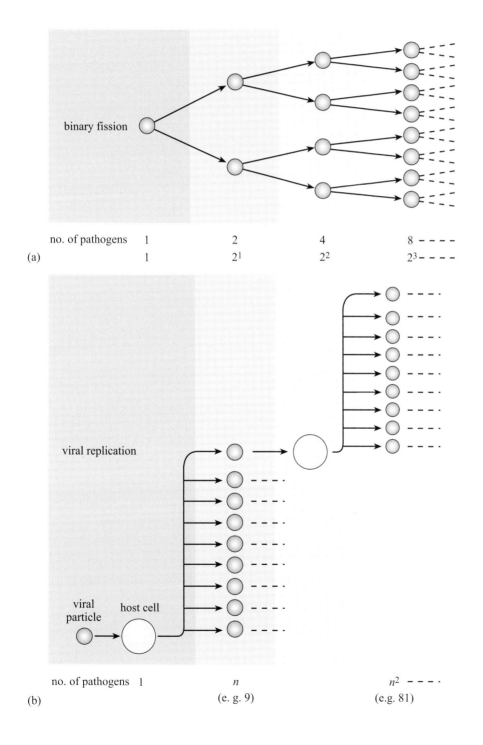

FIGURE 3.11
Increase in numbers of bacteria and viruses.

Consider first a bacterium that divides by binary fission. This means that each bacterium produces two new bacteria which then divide to produce four bacteria and so on (Figure 3.11). This doubling method of reproduction gives bacteria a characteristic population dynamic, at least in the early stages of increase when there is nothing to limit its increase.

In Book 2, p. 39, it was noted that *E. coli* may divide once every 20 minutes (referred to as the doubling time) although for other species it may be much longer. In contrast, on the same page of Book 2, the doubling time for lymphocytes, the host's cells mediating the adaptive immune response, is about six hours. What are the quantitative implications of this imbalance in doubling time?

○ Assume a bacterium has a doubling time of 30 minutes and that we start with one individual. How many are present after six hours, i.e. the time taken for a lymphocyte to divide?

● After 30 minutes there will be two individuals, after one hour there will be four, after 90 minutes there will be eight and so on. After six hours there will be a staggering 4096 bacteria (but only two lymphocytes).

There are two ways of calculating the number of bacteria after six hours. You can either keep doubling the numbers after every 30 minutes, i.e. repeat the calculation 12 times in total. This is rather time-consuming! Or, to speed the process up, you can note that after one 30-minute period there are 2^1 (2 to the power 1, i.e. 2) individuals, after two 30-minute periods there are 2^2 (2 to the power 2, i.e. 4) and so on. So, after twelve 30-minute periods (6 hours), there are 2^{12} bacteria, which is 4096.

Thus, any delay in detection of the bacteria by the host will result in a considerable numerical disadvantage to the host.

○ Do you imagine that bacteria could maintain that rate of population increase?

● No, otherwise the world would be covered with the species of bacterium with the shortest doubling time! Competition between individuals (and between species) will limit availability of resources and will result in the slowing of the population increase. Eventually, interactions with the host defence system (see Book 3) will also lead to a slowing down of the increase and even a reduction in numbers of the pathogen.

Let us consider a second example of pathogen increase in the host. In this case, we will go back to Chapter 2 of Book 1 and look at the influenza virus. Recall that antibody production against the virus begins 3 to 4 days after infection. Eventually, this may lead to elimination of the virus. But what numbers of the virus are present by the time that antibody production kicks in?

Viruses replicate by infecting a host cell and then producing multiple copies of themselves (Figure 3.11) that are released (usually) by lysing the host cell. Therefore, after each replication cycle, the number of viruses multiply by a certain number.

To estimate the number of virus particles after three days, we need to know three variables – the number of virions (V) at the start of infection (denoted by V_0, i.e. the number at time zero), the average number of virions produced per host cell (r) and the average time taken for replication (t). Before dealing with the specific values for influenza, let us generate a simple formula that could be used for any virus.

○ What is the average number of viral replication cycles in 3 days?

● $3/t$. But we need to be careful with the units! If the viral replication time is expressed in hours, then the total time under consideration also needs to be in hours. Thus, if viral replication time was 12 hours, the number of viral replications would be $72/12 = 6$.

In order to generalize, we will replace the number of hours over which replication is taking place (72 above) by T. Thus there are T/t replication cycles. If each viral replication produces r virions, then the equation for the number of virions after T hours (denoted by V_T) is:

> no. of virions after T hours (V_T) = no. at start (V_0) × no. produced per replication cycle (r) to the power T/t, or
>
> $V_T = V_0 \times r^{T/t}$ (Eqn 3.2)

This uses the same logic as our bacterial example. In that case, the number of replication cycles was the number of doubling periods ($12 = 6/0.5$). The number of bacteria produced per replication cycle was 2, i.e. r was 2.

So Equation 3.2 is sufficiently general to be able to predict the number of bacteria after a fixed period of time (B_T), knowing the initial number (B_0) and the doubling time t. Equations of this type are used widely in ecology to describe the increase in the number of organisms over time, with the assumption that there is no limit to the rates of increase.

Summary of Section 3.4

1   The reproduction rates of bacteria and viruses are discussed in relation to the response times of the human host.

2   The number of bacteria and viruses produced after a given time can be described by a simple equation, given the initial number, duration of replication and number of offspring produced.

3.5 The role of other species in the ecology of human diseases

3.5.1 Host–pathogen communities

Earlier examples in this book have made it clear that many other species, in addition to human hosts and pathogens, are frequently involved in host–pathogen interactions. Indeed, in many cases it is not a simple host-pathogen interaction but a three-way or more interaction. This extends the area of study into **community ecology** that addresses the dynamics and other properties (such as relative abundance of species) arising from interactions of many species. An ecological community can be defined as a set of species, populations of which may interact with each other over a given area. We have already seen many ways in which hosts and pathogens may interact, not only with each other, but also with alternative or intermediate hosts and vectors. These interactions are summarized in Figure 3.12. We will adopt the shorthand of referring to these as **host–pathogen communities** (which may include intermediate or secondary hosts and vectors). The interactions within the host–pathogen community are generally played out over small areas, e.g. in the case of malaria it is limited by the flight of the female mosquito that in turn is linked to the availability of habitat for egg laying. This is not always the case, especially in human examples where infected milk or meat, or the hosts themselves, may travel hundreds of miles, thereby potentially spreading the range of the community. These host–pathogen communities, and ecological communities in general, may be described as more or less diverse, depending on the number of interacting species and their relative abundance in the community (Box 3.3).

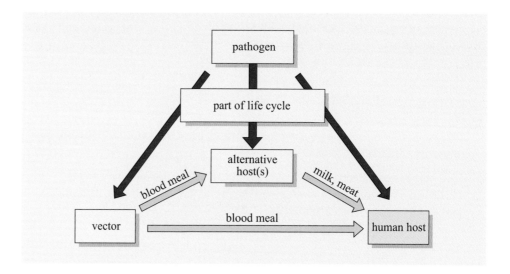

FIGURE 3.12
Generalized interactions within the host–pathogen communities.

In reviewing the role of other species, we should revisit the concept of zoonoses introduced in Book 1 and Chapter 1 of this book.

○ Recall from Book 1, Box 1.2, the definition of zoonoses (singular: zoonosis).

● A disease caused by an infection that can be transmitted to humans from other vertebrates under naturally occurring conditions. This link is represented in Figure 3.12 by the arrow from alternative host(s) to human host.

BOX 3.3   Diversity of ecological communities

The term diversity is often used rather loosely to refer to the variety of species in an ecological community. In fact, ecologists recognize two components of diversity: richness and evenness. Richness is a measure of the number of different species in an assemblage. For example, this might be the number of hosts of the *Ixodes* tick larvae (see Figure 2.7 for details). Evenness, as the name implies, is a measure of the relative abundance of these different species. Again, with reference to the tick example, there may be four hosts (species richness is four), one of which is ten times more abundant than the other three combined. This would be a highly uneven community. Abundance can be measured as number of individuals (preferably as population density) or amount of biomass. You may come across ecological measures of diversity, i.e. indices that represent the degree of diversity in a community. These indices combine measures of richness and evenness. High richness and even abundance contribute to a high diversity value.

Here we will examine in more detail the various types of zoonosis. They can be classified into four groups depending in part on the manner of transmission: direct zoonoses, cyclozoonoses, metazoonoses and saprozoonoses.

Direct zoonoses involve transmission from the vertebrate host to a susceptible human by direct contact, fomite or by a mechanical vector. In this example, there is no developmental change or propagation of the organism during transmission. Examples of direct zoonoses include rabies and brucellosis. **Cyclozoonoses** require more than one vertebrate host but no invertebrate host and include human tapeworm infections (Book 2, Section 7.4). In **metazoonoses**, the agent multiplies and/or develops in an invertebrate host before transmission to a vertebrate host is possible. Examples include arboviruses, plague and schistosomiasis.

- ☐ Why is malaria not an example of metazoonosis?
- ⬤ Because, although the pathogen develops and multiplies in an invertebrate vector during transmission, it is usually transmitted between humans and not from a vertebrate host.

The final category of zoonoses are **saprozoonoses**. In this case, non-animal development sites or reservoirs are required, such as food plants, soil or other organic material. Examples in this category include some mycotic diseases.

3.5.2 Radiation of host–pathogen communities

Examples such as HIV show that pathogens are continually switching to new hosts. In so doing, they are creating new host–pathogen communities. One way of understanding the changing patterns of host–pathogen communities is to consider the different communities that have arisen amongst closely related pathogen species. In evolutionary terms, we can talk about the **radiation** of host–pathogen communities, in the same way that one might discuss the radiation of non-pathogen species, e.g. Darwin's finches in the Galapagos islands. The species of trypanosome provide an excellent example of the radiation of host–pathogen communities.

☐ Recall from Book 2 the characteristics and different types of trypanosome.

⬤ Trypanosomes are single-celled, animal-like cells with flagella. They include *Trypanosoma* species that cause a variety of diseases including trypanosomiasis (sleeping sickness). Another group of trypansomes are in the genus *Leishmania*, which cause a whole series of different types of disease.

The extraordinary diversity of host–pathogen communities associated with *Trypanosoma* and *Leishmania* are illustrated in Figure 3.13. For *Trypanosoma*, the interactions include a variety of vectors, especially flies (*Glossina* species – which includes tsetse flies – and horseflies or tabanids) and, in stark contrast, a reduvid bug which is the vector for Chagas' disease. The other vertebrates involved in these communities include semi-domesticated stock (horses, donkeys, cattle, camels) and wild animals (antelope and deer). Some of the communities do not include humans and the diseases that characterize them are diseases of the other vertebrates. In one case, there is no vector (dourine acute).

The communities associated with *Trypanosoma* show interesting geographical patterns. For example, the subspecies of *Trypanosoma brucei* in East Africa is transmitted by *Glossina morsitans* and causes acute sleeping sickness. In West Africa, another subspecies of *T. brucei* (*gambiense*) is transmitted by another *Glossina* species (*Glossina pallipides*, tsetse fly) and causes chronic sleeping sickness. Finally, a third subspecies of *T. brucei* (*brucei*) is widely distributed in Africa, transmitted by the tsetse fly, and causes a disease in domestic stock and wild animals (nagana acute). To complicate the story further, this same disease appears to be caused by two other *Trypanosoma* species (*vivax* and *congolense*), spread by *Glossina morsitans*. The relatively subtle shifts in trypanosome vector in Africa (e.g. between *Glossina* species) contrasts with the one New World example, where the vector is an entirely different order of insect.

The *Leishmania* communities in both the New and Old World all involve sandflies with at least five different pathogen species and three forms of the disease.

☐ What major difference in the composition of *Leishmania* and *Trypanosoma* associated communities is apparent from Figure 3.13?

⬤ *Leishmania* communities do not have an alternative vertebrate host, in contrast to all the *Trypanosoma* communities.

Interpretation of the evolutionary and ecological patterns of host–pathogen communities has been helped enormously by the analysis of phylogenetic trees (or phylogenies) derived from molecular data (RNA or DNA sequence data, e.g. from ribosomal RNA, rRNA). These trees show not only what is related to what but also the closeness of that relationship. The statistical analyses used to construct these trees are extremely complex and cannot be covered here. However, the cautionary tale is that there may be many, equally likely phylogenetic trees. Thus we should treat a phylogenetic tree as the latest in a series of hypotheses about the relationship between the species in question.

FIGURE 3.13 (Opposite) Global radiation of host–trypanosome communities.

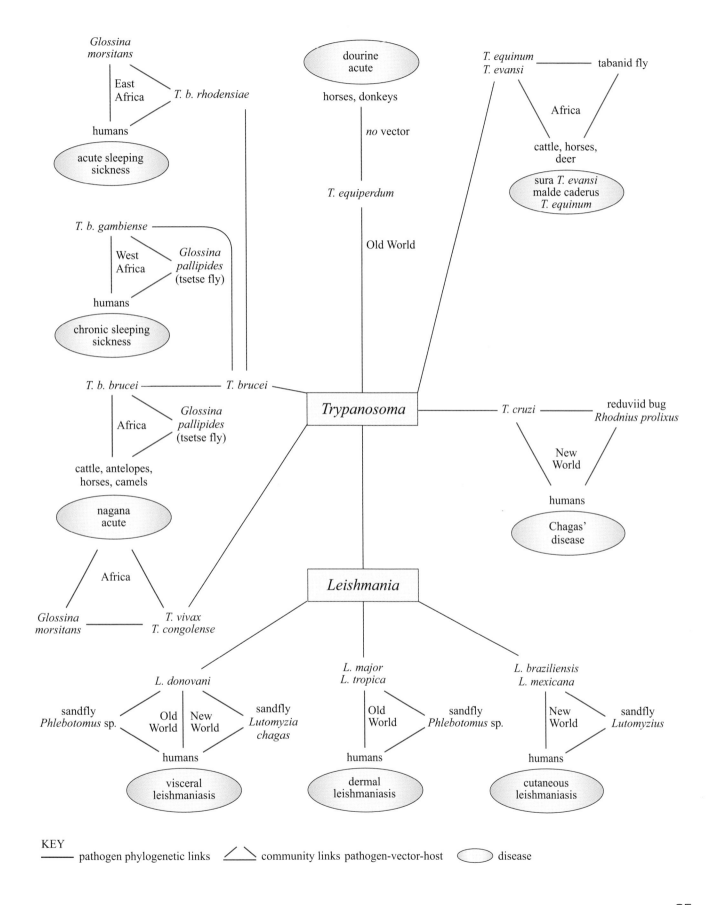

KEY
— pathogen phylogenetic links   ⟨△⟩ community links pathogen-vector-host   ⬭ disease

The other important result that can be derived from the phylogenetic tree is the age of the relationships, i.e. given certain assumptions (such as the rate of mutation) the time before present at which species diverged can be estimated. Therefore, in theory we should be able to estimate how many million years ago *Leishmania* split from *Trypanosoma* (assuming they are both derived from a common ancestor).

The phylogenetic tree for trypanosomes (current in 1999) is shown in Figure 3.14. This showed that the trypanosomes were monophyletic, i.e. derived from a common ancestor. It also showed the ancient divergence of the so-called 'aquatic clade' from other groups. (A clade is a group of closely related species with a common ancestor.) The aquatic clade comprises species of trypanosome found in marine and freshwater fish and amphibia. These trypanosomes are spread by aquatic leeches. Indeed, one of the important findings of the phylogenetic analysis is to show the coevolution of the pathogens and their vectors – thus, closely related trypanosomes (comprising a single clade) tend to be transmitted by the same closely related set of vectors. But we also predict that the trypanosomes will coevolve with their vertebrate hosts. This has also been supported by the phylogenetic studies, for example, most of the *T. cruzi* clade are associated with South American mammals. The exceptions to this are an unnamed species that infects kangaroos and two species of European bat trypanosomes.

○ Why would the kangaroo and European bat trypanosomes be related to the other *T. cruzi* affected species?

● In the case of the kangaroo, this is because Australia was joined to South America via Antarctica much later than South America was joined to Africa. Thus, the *T. cruzi* clade may have evolved across South America, Antarctica and Australia. The European bats are mobile and may have been able to disperse over long distances (possibly linking South America and Africa).

The dating of the divergence of these clades suggests that trypanosomes have coevolved with their hosts over several hundred million years. For example, the *T. brucei* clade is predicted to have diverged from other clades during the Permian, when reptiles were the most advanced vertebrates and certainly when none of the current hosts were present. Therefore, as humans evolved in Africa, they were amongst trypanosomes whose evolution was already several hundred million years old and for which movement into a new (and increasingly abundant) primate host was simply a matter of time. In South America, as humans migrated into the continent 30 000–40 000 years ago, the *T. cruzi* trypanosomes also had a short host leap from their existing host range, which included primates.

Finally, consideration of the host–pathogen community is vital for understanding the reasons for changes in incidence of disease. For example, construction of the Aswan High Dam resulted in huge increases in the prevalence of *Schistosoma mansoni*, from 5% in 1968 to 77% in 1993. This was largely due to an increase in the snail intermediate hosts that benefited from the increased habitat associated with the dam and irrigation channels. Deforestation in Africa has also favoured *Anopheles gambiae*, by increasing its habitat. Understanding the host–pathogen community is also vital for understanding emerging infectious diseases.

○ Recall from Book 2 the missing information on the host–pathogen community of the Ebola virus.

● Ebola is a zoonosis, but the animal that carries it has not been found.

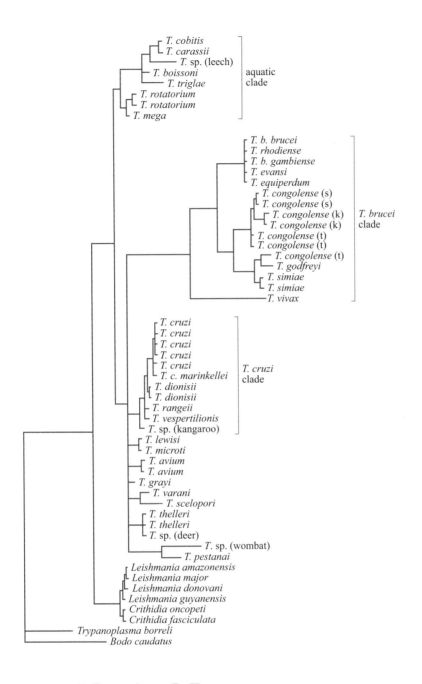

FIGURE 3.14
Phylogenetic tree of trypanosomes.

Summary of Section 3.5

1   Hosts and pathogens can be linked in various ways to comprise host–pathogen communities. These communities include zoonoses, classified into four groups depending in part on the manner of transmission: direct zoonoses, cyclozoonoses, metazoonoses and saprozoonoses.

2   The radiation of host–pathogen communities is illustrated by the global radiation of host–trypanosome communities. Understanding the patterns of radiation is aided by a detailed phylogenetic tree.

3   The incidence of disease in humans can often only be understood with reference to the whole host–pathogen community.

3.6 Ecological attributes of host–pathogen interactions

The compartmental model of malaria infection and the potential cycling in abundance of pathogen populations showed that the emergent dynamic properties of the host–pathogen system depend on details of the interactions between all the linked populations. In this final section, we will summarize aspects of the ecology (and biology) of the individuals and populations that characterize host–pathogen interactions and influence most heavily the abundance of the pathogen. In so doing, we will draw together material from Chapter 1 on life-history strategies, Chapter 2 on co-evolution and from earlier books in this course.

3.6.1 Body size

In all host–pathogen interactions, the host is very large compared to the pathogen. Where vectors are involved, the vector is of intermediate size. **Body size** is important for two reasons. The most apparent is one of physical constraints. A pathogen needs to survive and reproduce within or amongst the physiological apparatus of its host. In the most extreme examples – such as viruses – the pathogens need to access molecules such as enzymes, ATP and amino acids from within the cell of its host. This provides a clear constraint on pathogen size.

Secondly, body size is strongly correlated with the generation time of the organism. The smaller the body size, the more rapid the generation time. The pathogen needs to have a more rapid generation time than its host. Otherwise, it will fail to reproduce before the host dies.

In many host–pathogen interactions, the pathogen needs to have a much more rapid generation time than that of its host. This is because it needs to reproduce before the host's defence system has detected it. Ideally, it will have completed several replication cycles (Section 3.4) before the body has begun to respond – the rate of detection depending on the number of Tc cells in the body.

3.6.2 Active transmission

Many of the most effective pathogens use active forms of transmission from host to host. This includes employment of insect vectors and causing changes in the host's physiology and/or behaviour to elicit transmission.

○ Can you give an example of changes in the human host's physiology and/or behaviour caused by the pathogen that favour its transmission?

● Examples include sneezing (influenza), skin lesions (cowpox, smallpox) and diarrhoea (see Section 2.4 for more details).

These changes in host physiology and behaviour may also be linked to using waste products of hosts (urine, faeces) and causing a more rapid expulsion of these products as was illustrated for the *Vibrio cholerae* bacterium in Book 2 (p. 10). These changes may also be associated with a site-specificity on the host that maximizes transmission, e.g. around the genitalia – as noted in the *Syphilis* Case Study, humans find it hard to avoid reproducing (or at least attempting it). Transmission may also be increased by aggregation of the host, leading to a higher local density of hosts (see Section 3.1). Aggregation may be due to work (e.g.

malaria spreading through mining communities), poor and crowded housing (TB), lack of sanitation (cholera) or social behaviour (STIs, including HIV). Note that multiple sexual partners constitute a form of aggregation – not necessarily aggregation in one place at one time (!) but aggregation over a short time period.

The ecological parallel of transmission in populations that are not pathogenic is dispersal from one suitable habitat to another. Many of the most abundant species in the world are those that can successfully move from one habitat patch to another. This is especially true today with the increasing fragmentation of habitats. A patchy habitat is essentially what the pathogen experiences – a habitat comprised of a set of individual hosts separated in space. In this way, it is no different from a fly species that reproduces in patches of dung. It must first find the dung, lay eggs in it, complete its life cycle before the dung dries out and then move on to the next pile.

We have emphasized the active aspects of transmission. But what is passive transmission and are there any examples amongst pathogens? In passive transmission, pathogens will return to the environment and be picked up by passing hosts. This environment might include areas of soil, vegetation and water bodies. Ticks (and other ectoparasites, e.g. leeches) use this method of dispersal between hosts. They feed on a host, drop off into the vegetation or soil and then later get picked up by a passing host. In some cases, they may move a short distance to maximize their chances of a pick-up (they are part active). Whilst these ectoparasites are not infectious agents, they can be vectors of infectious agents, such as Lyme disease (Book 2 and Chapter 2 of this book).

3.6.3 Co-occurrence

Pathogens need to occur in the same areas and habitats as their hosts. We have already seen how some pathogens exist within a smaller fraction of the geographical range of their host (Section 3.1). One way that pathogens can increase their chances of interaction with their host is to exploit the resources required by the host, i.e. water and food. Alternatively, the pathogens exploit vectors or intermediate hosts associated with these resources.

- ☐ Can you give two examples of vectors or intermediate hosts associated with water bodies?

- ⬤ *Anopheles* mosquitoes (malaria vector) and aquatic snails (schistosomiasis or bilharzia intermediate host).

In both these examples, the vectors and pathogens are associated with water bodies close to human habitation or places of work (thereby increasing co-occurrence). In the case of schistosomiasis, the cercariae and their vectors are especially prevalent in irrigated fields where crops are grown or shallow rivers where people wash. Pathogens and vectors associated with water bodies are of enormous global importance in terms of the numbers of humans infected and the amounts of mortality or serious illness. Of particular note is the number of diseases associated with mosquito transmission (dengue, malaria, filariasis, yellow fever). When one extends this to other biting Diptera (flies), thereby including leishmaniasis (sandflies) and onchocerciasis (blackflies), the importance of water as breeding areas for flies as vectors of disease becomes overwhelming (Figures 3.15, 3.16). The reasons for the success of the pathogens that cause these diseases lies in their utilization of a vector that lives part of its life in water and part of its life aerially, feeding off humans. The pathogen therefore maintains an intimate relationship with both the individual host and one of his/her most essential dietary and domestic requirements: water. Moreover, these Diptera are able to utilize water bodies created by their hosts.

There are also examples of pathogens that are not exclusively associated with water and may be spread through contaminated food. Ascariasis, typhoid (*Salmonella typhi*) and cholera are all spread via food (contaminated hands, flies or utensils) and water contaminated with faeces and/or urine (in all cases, transmitted through the faecal–oral route, Book 2, p. 18). Thus, the resources of food and water are linked in these examples.

(a)

(b)

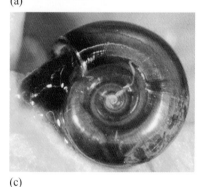

(c)

(d)

FIGURE 3.15
Co-occurence of human hosts with vectors or intermediate hosts associated with water:
(a) blackfly, showing mouthparts;
(b) sandfly;
(c) *Biomphalaria* snail; and
(d) workers in a rice paddy field.

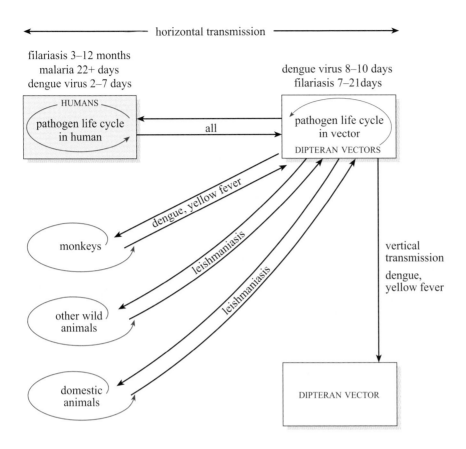

FIGURE 3.16 Summary of host–pathogen communities associated with dipteran vectors with aquatic stages.

3.6.4 Specialization

It is expected that pathogens will specialize on one or a few closely related hosts. This prediction results from a consideration of co-evolution (Chapter 2), with pathogens evolving ever more complex methods of living in hosts and overcoming their defences. The evolutionary responses of the hosts ensure that many pathogens become locked into an increasingly specialized relationship with one host or a few host species. Again, there are ecological parallels amongst non-pathogenic species. For example, herbivorous insects often specialize on plant species that are highly toxic to generalist predators. Through co-evolution, the plant feeders have overcome the defence systems of the plant (and the plant may have, in turn, evolved more toxic defence systems – which the herbivores have evolved to overcome, and so on). In some cases, the herbivores have used plant defence to their advantage, i.e. to defend themselves.

3.6.5 Overview and implications for emerging diseases

The four criteria listed in this section represent ecological and evolutionary constraints on the parasites and hosts. One can take the argument further and predict the most effective pathogens based on maximizing or minimizing these constraints. Thus, we would predict that the most abundant ('successful') pathogens would be those in which:

- body size is minimized (and replication rate is maximized);

- active transmission and co-occurrence are maximized;

- host (or part of host) specialization is maximized (especially with respect to defence against hosts or detection by hosts).

However, this is overly simplistic and we need to consider trade-offs. For example, smaller body size may be beneficial for faster replication but also carries costs if genome size is reduced. This is apparent in viruses: those with large genomes carry sophisticated host defence countermeasures, but replicate slowly. Viruses with small genomes rely on fast replication and have no spare genes for defence countermeasures.

○ Are there any other criteria that we have discussed in this chapter that might also feature in this list?

● Dormancy, discussed in Section 3.3.

Another way of looking at these criteria (implied above) is that they represent an evolutionary route for pathogens. Thus, we might predict that pathogens will evolve from large to small body size, from passive to active transmission, from high to low detection and generalist to specialist.

This concluding section of this book complements the discussion of Chapter 1, Section 1.3.4, where we attempted to identify the life-history strategies of pathogens according to their within-host and between-host attributes. We now have a complementary set of ecological attributes. Body size is important for within-host dynamics because it affects reproductive rate, survival and movement in the host. Active or passive transmission is clearly relevant to between-host variables. Co-occurrence is relevant to between-host variables, ensuring that all the members of the host–pathogen community coexist in the same place at the same time. Finally, specialization, through coevolution, underpins the host defence countermeasures of the pathogen.

Summary of Section 3.6

1   Four important ecological attributes of host–pathogen interactions are identified that impact on the dynamics of the pathogen and contribute to the incidence of the disease.

2   Pathogen body size affects both the ability to survive and reproduce in the host and the generation time of the pathogen.

3   Pathogens generally employ forms of active transmission (vectors, changes in host physiology and/or behaviour) to move between hosts.

4   Pathogens enhance their chances of transmission by occurring in the same habitat as their hosts and, where applicable, their vectors. Pathogens associated with water bodies are a globally important example of this phenomenon, especially those linked to dipteran vectors with aquatic and terrestrial life history stages.

5   Based on considerations of coevolution, many pathogens are expected to be (or become) highly specialized, utilizing one or a few closely related host species.

6   The implications of these ecological attributes for the evolution of host–pathogen interactions and emerging infectious disease are discussed.

Learning Outcomes for Chapter 3

When you have completed this chapter, you should be able to:

3.1 Define and use, or recognize definitions and applications of, each of the terms printed in **bold** in the text. (*Question 3.1*)

3.2 Describe the geographical range of a host and its pathogen. (*Question 3.2*)

3.3 Interpret data on pathogen abundance patterns. (*Question 3.2*)

3.4 Interpret a simple compartmental model of host–pathogen dynamics. (*Question 3.2*)

3.5 Discuss the possible explanations for the fluctuations and cycling in abundance of some pathogen populations. (*Question 3.3*)

3.6 Distinguish between the different types of zoonosis. (*Question 3.1*)

3.7 Describe the composition, structure and evolutionary radiation of selected host–pathogen communities. (*Question 3.4*)

3.8 Describe and provide examples of the main ecological attributes of host–pathogen interactions. (*Question 3.5*)

Questions for Chapter 3

Question 3.1

Anthrax is commonly seen in cattle, sheep, horses, pigs and goats. These herbivorous animals are infected by ingestion of spores which are viable in soil for years. Humans are infected by handling contaminated carcasses, wool or hides and by ingestion or inhalation of the spores or bacteria (*Bacillis anthracis*). What category of zoonosis does anthrax fit best?

Question 3.2

Describe how the malaria compartmental model gives information on patterns of pathogen abundance and range.

Question 3.3

Why is the malaria compartmental model unlikely to lead to constant levels of pathogens over time?

Question 3.4

Based on trypanosome host–pathogen communities in the Old World, what predictions can be made about the future evolution of trypanosome communities in the New World?

Question 3.5

Why might co-occurrence with the host and host specialization not be important features in pathogens of emerging diseases?

REFERENCES

General reading

Anderson, R. M. and May, R. M. (1992) *Infectious Diseases of Humans*, Oxford University Press.

Ewald, P. W. (2000) *Plague Time*, The Free Press, New York.

Hudson, P. J., Rizzoli, A., Grenfell, B. T., Heesterbeek, H. and Dobson, A. P. (eds) (2002) *The Ecology of Wildlife Diseases*, Oxford University Press.

Karlen, A. (1995) *Plague's Progress. A Social History of Man and Disease*, Victor Gollancz, London.

Stearns, S. C. (1999) Introducing evolutionary thinking, in: *Evolution in Health and Disease,* S. C. Stearns (ed.) Oxford University Press, pp. 161–172.

Specific reading (chapter reference given in brackets)

Anderson, D. I. and Levin, B. R. (1999) The biological cost of antibiotic resistance, *Current Opinion in Microbiology*, **2**, pp. 489–493. *(Chapter 2)*

Austin, D. J., Kristinsson, K. G. and Anderson, R. M. (1999) The relationship between the volume of antimicrobial consumption in human communities and the frequency of resistance, *Proc. Natl. Acad. Sci. USA*, **96**, pp. 1152–1156. *(Chapter 2)*

Blount, J. D., Houston, D. C. and Møller, A. P. (2000) Why egg yolk is yellow, *Trends in Ecology and Evolution*, **15**, pp. 47–49. *(Chapter 1)*

Bull, J. J. (1994) Virulence, *Evolution*, **48**, pp. 1423–1437. *(Chapter 2)*

Bunyard, P. (2002) Breeding the superbug, *The Ecologist*, **32**, pp. 32–37. *(Chapter 2)*

Caren, L. D. (1991) Effects of exercise on the human immune system, *BioScience*, **41**, pp. 410–415. *(Chapter 1)*

Carey, C. (2000) Infectious disease and worldwide declines of amphibian populations, with comments on emerging diseases in coral reef organisms and in humans, *Environmental Health Perspectives*, **108** (Suppl. 1), pp. 143–150. *(Chapter 1)*

Chandler, M. and Claverys, J.-P. (2001) Genome diversity: sources and forces, *Current Opinion in Microbiology*, **4**, pp. 547–549. *(Chapter 2)*

Cleaveland, S., Laurenson, M. K. and Taylor, L. H. (2001) Diseases of humans and their domestic mammals: pathogen characteristics, host range and the risk of emergence, *Phil. Trans. Roy Soc. Lond. B*, **356**, pp. 991–999. *(Chapter 1)*

Colwell, R. R. (1996) Global climate change and infectious disease, *Science*, **274**, pp. 2025–2031. *(Chapter 3)*

Cowden, J. M. (2002) Winter vomiting, *British Medical Journal*, **324**, pp. 249–250. *(Chapter 1)*

Czárán, T. L., Hoekstra, R. F. and Pagie, L. (2002) Chemical warfare between microbes promotes biodiversity, *Proc. Natl. Acad. Sci. USA*, **99**, pp. 786–790. *(Chapter 1)*

Day, T. (2001) Parasite transmission modes and the evolution of virulence, *Evolution*, **55**, pp. 2389–2400. *(Chapters 1 and 2)*

Dobson, A. P. (1996) *Conservation and Biodiversity*, W. H. Freeman, New York. *(Chapter 1)*

Feil, E. J. and Spratt, B. G. (2001) Recombination and the population structures of bacterial pathogens, *Ann. Rev. Microbiol.*, **55**, pp. 561–590. *(Chapter 2)*

Fitzgerald, L. (1988) Exercise and the immune system, *Immunology Today,* **9**, pp. 337–339. *(Chapter 1)*

Fitzgerald, J. R. and Musser, J. M. (2001) Evolutionary genomics of pathogenic bacteria, *Trends in Microbiology*, **9**, pp. 547–553. *(Chapter 2)*

Gandon, S., van Baalen, M. and Jansen, V. A. A. (2002) The evolution of parasite virulence, superinfection, and host resistance, *Amer. Natur.*, **159**, pp. 658–669. *(Chapter 2)*

Gavazzi, G. and Krause, K.-H. (2002) Ageing and infection, *The Lancet Infectious Diseases*, **2**, pp. 659–666. *(Chapter 1)*

Gould, S. J. and Lewontin, R. C. (1979) The spandrels of San Marco and the Panglossian paradigm: a critique of the adaptationist program, *Proc. Roy. Soc. Lond. B*, **205**, pp. 581–598. *(Chapter 2)*

Gubler, D. J. (1998) Resurgent vector-borne diseases as a global health problem, *Emerging Infectious Diseases*, **4**. *(Chapters 2 and 3)*

Hawksworth, D. L. (1992) Microorganisms, in: *Global Biodiversity*, World Conservation Monitoring Centre, Chapman & Hall, London. *(Chapter 1)*

Hill, A. V. S. (2001) The genomics and genetics of human infectious disease susceptibility, *Ann. Rev. Genomics Human Genet.*, **2**, pp. 373–400. *(Chapter 2)*

Holmes, J. C. (1983) Evolutionary relationships between parasitic helminths and their hosts, in: Futuyma, D. J. and Slatkin, M. (eds) *Coevolution*, Sinauer, Sunderland, Mass., pp. 161–185. *(Chapter 2)*

Hughes, A. L. (2002) Evolution of the host defense system, in: *Immunology of Infectious Diseases.*, Kaufmann, S. H. E., Sher, A. and Ahmed, R. (eds), ASM Press, Washington DC, USA, pp. 67–75. *(Chapter 2)*

Hughes, K. A., Alipaz, J. A., Drnevich, J. M. and Reynolds, R. M. (2002) A test of evolutionary theories of aging, *Proc. Natl. Acad. Sci. USA*, **99**, pp. 14286–14291. *(Chapter 1)*

Jones, S. (1996) *In The Blood*, Harper Collins, London. *(Chapter 2)*

Kerr, C. (2002) Bloodsucking fly blamed for transmitting HIV, *The Lancet Infectious Diseases*, **2**, p. 265. *(Chapter 2)*

Levin, B. R. (1996) The evolution and maintenance of virulence in microparasites, *Emerging Infectious Diseases*, **2**. *(Chapter 2).*

Levy, S. B. (2001) Antibacterial household products: cause for concern, *J. Emerging Infectious Diseases*, **7**, pp. 512–515. *(Chapter 2)*

Lockhart, A. B., Thrall, P. H. and Antonovics, J. (1996) Sexually transmitted diseases in animals: ecological and evolutionary implications, *Biol. Rev.*, **71**, pp. 415–471. *(Chapters 2 and 3)*

Lycett, G. J. and Kafatos, F. C. (2002) Anti-malarial mosquitoes?, *Nature*, **417**, pp. 387–388. *(Chapters 2 and 3)*

May, R, M. and Anderson, R, M. (1978) Regulation and stability of host–parasite population interactions. II. Destabilising processes, *J. Anim. Ecol*, **47**, pp. 249–267. *(Chapters 1 and 3)*

Merrell, D. S., Butler, S. M., Qadri, F., Dolganov, N. A., Alam, A., Cohen, M. B., Calderwood, S. B., Schoolnik, G. K. and Camilli, A. (2002) Host-induced epidemic spread of the cholera bacterium, *Nature*, **417**, pp. 642–645. *(Chapters 2 and 3)*

Moore, S. L. and Wilson, K. (2002) Parasites as a viability cost of sexual selection in natural populations of mammals, *Science*, **297**, pp. 2015–2018. *(Chapter 1)*

Norris, K. and Evans, M. R. (2000) Ecological immunity: life history trade-offs and immune defense in birds, *Behav. Ecol*, **11**, pp. 19–26. *(Chapter 1)*

Ostfeld, R. S. and Keesing, F. (2000) Biodiversity and disease risk: the case of Lyme disease, *Conservation Biology*, **14**, pp. 722–728. *(Chapters 1 and 3)*

Pearce, F. (2002) Dung to death, *New Scientist*, 20 April, 15. *(Chapter 2)*

Penn, D. J., Damjanovich, K. and Potts, W. K. (2002) MHC heterozygosity confers a selective advantage against multiple-strain infections, *Proc. Natl. Acad. Sci. USA*, **99**, pp. 11260–11264. *(Chapter 2)*

Poulin, R. (2000) Manipulation of host behaviour by parasites: a weakening paradigm, *Proc. Roy. Soc. Lond. B*, **267**, p. 787. *(Chapter 2)*

Ridley, M. (1999) *Genome*, Fourth Estate, London. *(Chapter 2)*

Rigby, M. C., Hechinger, R. F. and Stevens, L. (2002) Why should parasite resistance be costly?, *Trends in Parasitology*, **18** (3), pp. 116–120. *(Chapter 1)*

Smith, D. L., Harris, A. D., Johnson, J. A., Silbergeld, E. K. and Morris, J. G. (2002) Animal antibiotic use has an early but important impact on the emergence of antibiotic resistance in human commensal bacteria, *Proc. Natl. Acad. Sci. USA*, **99**, pp. 6434–6439. *(Chapter 2)*

Steen, H., Taitt, M. and Krebs, C. J. (2002) Risk of parasite-induced predation: an experimental field study on Townsend's voles (*Microtus townsendii*), *Can. J. Zool.*, **80**, pp. 1286–1292. *(Chapters 1 and 3)*

Stevens, L., Giordano, R. and Fialho, R. F. (2001) Male-killing, nematode infections, bacteriophage infection, and virulence of cytoplasmic bacteria in the genus *Wolbachia*, *Ann. Rev. Ecol. Syst.*, **32**, pp. 519–545. *(Chapter 2)*

Taylor, L. H., Latham, S. M. and Woolhouse, M. E. J. (2001) Risk factors for human disease emergence, *Phil. Trans. Roy. Soc. Lond. B*, **356**, pp. 983–989. *(Chapter 1)*

ANSWERS TO QUESTIONS

QUESTION 1.1

Arguments for using the term pathogen. The course is concerned with infectious disease and as pathogen means causing harm (damage to host tissue) this is most appropriate, as opposed to parasite which includes any organism that lives in or on its host (irrespective of any damage it may cause). Pathogens are a sub-set of parasites. *Arguments against using the term pathogen.* The term parasite tends to be used in the ecological and evolutionary literature to include pathogens. This presents a problem for both you and the Course Team when searching the literature. However, as long as we are aware of that issue, using the term pathogen is most appropriate for a course on infectious disease.

QUESTION 1.2

Zoonoses are an obvious example. This may include pathogens that continue to be passed from animals to humans (e.g. vCJD) or pathogens that have previously crossed the host species barrier and are now routinely transmitted between human hosts (e.g. HIV). Ebola is an example of a zoonosis whose vertebrate host is unknown. Vector-borne diseases also warrant study of the pathogens not only in the vectors but also in alternative vertebrate hosts.

QUESTION 1.3

The normal life history of humans (in common with many vertebrates) is birth, growth, reproduction (possibly several times) and death. Pathogens also go through this sequence, but may reproduce only once (or many times). Reproduction may also vary in the number of offspring produced – possibly hundreds or thousands. The most important difference is that the life history of pathogens has to include transmission between hosts. Transmission events may occur at different points in the life history, e.g. during the juvenile (pre-reproductive stage). The whole life history may occur across several different hosts.

QUESTION 1.4

Cryptosporidium (Book 2, Figure 5.10) produces symptoms after 5 days, suggesting minimum duration in the host is short.

Trypanosoma brucei – trypanosomes have an outer protein coat (Book 2, p.101) and antigenic properties change. Minimum duration in the host is greater than 10 days. Transmission by insect vector.

Filarial roundworms have a minimum duration in human host of 3 months. Transmission by insect vector.

Herpes simplex. Direct host-to-host contact and long duration in host (>30 days). Remains undetected in nervous system.

Schistosomes. Long duration in host (>30 days and often for several years). Dispersal via water (can swim towards host).

TSEs. Long duration in host. Transmission is via consumption of infected meat (vertebrate or human host) so essentially host–host contact.

Given the above information, we can put the diseases into a new version of Table 1.4 (see Table A1.1):

TABLE A1.1 Pathogen life-history categories updated from Table 1.4 with the above diseases included **(bold)**.

		Within-host parameters		
	minimum duration in host	short (<10 days) (none)	medium (>10 days) (moderate)	long (>30 days) (complex)
Between-host (transmission) parameters	abiotic environment (air, soil, water)	influenza cholera *Cryptosporidium*		**schistosomes**
	vector		malaria *Trypanosoma brucei*	**filarial roundworms**
	host-to-host contact			syphilis, HIV, **herpes simplex, TSEs**

The inclusion of these six diseases fills in two more of the cells of the table but still suggests that this is a useful way of categorizing life-history strategies. In particular, it suggests that short duration in hosts and transmission by vector or host to host are not viable combinations for pathogens.

QUESTION 1.5

Reproductive status changes with age and it is expected that defence will be traded off against reproductive effort, especially under conditions of very low food availability.

QUESTION 2.1

The prudent pathogen model (and, ultimately, the incipient mutualism model). Virulence is defined as the ease of infection and the degree of damage. The prudent pathogen model predicts a reduction in damage to the host (and hence a reduction in virulence).

QUESTION 2.2

Sexual reproduction is identified (Section 2.2.1) as 'the major source' of genetic variation in large complex organisms such as humans (i.e. most hosts). Other sources of genetic variation are mutations and drift. Pathogens also show genetic variation due to mutation and drift but vary in terms of the amount of variation resulting from sexual reproduction. Some pathogens do not have sexual reproduction, although they may have other sources of genetic variation such as horizontal transfer.

QUESTION 2.3

In Section 2.4.1, three ways of looking at host manipulation are discussed. The third is possibly relevant to STIs: '… changes in the host caused by pathogen manipulation … are adaptive for the pathogen, e.g. in aiding transmission.' This would indeed be the case if pathogens caused increased sexual activity. However, there is no evidence for this (Section 2.5.1). Therefore, it seems that these pathogens use sexual activity as a means of transmission but do not increase its likelihood. Having said that, by having little effect on host physiology during (at least) the early stages of infection, the pathogens do not reduce the likelihood of sexual activity.

QUESTION 2.4

The guidelines would cover the following areas: to ensure that the use of antibiotics is limited to all but the clearest cases of need and to ensure that as soon as resistance is detected the antibiotic is withdrawn.

QUESTION 2.5

Diptera (flies) contain most vectors of human disease (see Table 2.3). There are several reasons for this, including the evolution of piercing mouthparts and the aquatic and aerial stages of the life cycle. The aquatic component is important because it brings the flies into close proximity with their hosts (see Chapter 3). The aerial (adult) stage allows the fly to seek out its host.

QUESTION 3.1

Based on the information given in the question, anthrax falls into one of two categories: direct zoonosis or saprozoonosis. It could be said to be a combination of both as it is found in the soil (in keeping with saprozoonoses, although there is no development) and usually is transmitted by direct contact with the carcass of the other host. It does not require more than one host (therefore ruling out cyclozoonoses) and does not require an invertebrate host (therefore ruling out metazoonoses).

QUESTION 3.2

The model does not give information on the abundance of pathogens in any one host or vector. Instead, it gives information on the number of hosts or vectors containing pathogens and whether those hosts or vectors are infectious. The model describes changes in abundance through time in one place (a hypothetical village) so does not tell us anything about range. It would be possible to construct a compartmental model at many different locations and then include movement between locations – but this is potentially a huge task!

QUESTION 3.3

The construction of the model produces an output that changes around a given threshold, e.g. a certain value of daily bite rate. If the threshold is exceeded, the pathogen population will increase and if the threshold is not reached the pathogen population will reduce. The model only predicts a constant level of pathogens if all the variables, such as daily bite rate, stay at a certain constant value over time. This is ecologically impossible. More-sophisticated models can produce predictions of stable pathogen populations (or fluctuations within narrow limits).

QUESTION 3.4

Further radiation of host–trypanosome communities is expected in the New World. First, we might expect more interactions with semi-domesticated stock (there are many examples of this in the Old World). Secondly, we might expect other vectors of the *Trypanosoma cruzi* clade to evolve, possibly transferring other members of the clade into human hosts. The vectors might be relatives of the reduviid bugs or, more likely, they may be biting fly species.

QUESTION 3.5

Emerging diseases are usually caused by pathogen species with which we have not previously had contact. This may be because we have not coexisted with their normal hosts (e.g. in dense forest) or because they cannot be transmitted from their normal hosts. Pathogen species with high host specificity are less likely to transfer to new (human) hosts.

ACKNOWLEDGEMENTS

Grateful acknowledgcment is made to the following sources for permission to reproduce material in this book:

Figures

Figure 1.1: Daszak, P. *et al.* (2000) 'Emerging infectious diseases of wildlife-threats to biodiversity and human health', *Science*, **287**, 21 January 2000. Copyright © 2000 by the American Association for the Advancement of Science; *Figure 1.2*: Lee Berger and Alex Hyatt, CSIRO Australian Animal Health Laboratory; *Figure 1.3*: Roitt, I., Brostoff, J. and Male, D. (1996) *Immunology*, 4th edn, Mosby International Ltd.; *Figure 1.4*: © The World Health Organisation; *Figure 1.5*: Mims *et al.*, *Medical Microbiology*, 2nd edn. Copyright © 1998 Mosby International Ltd.; *Figure 2.2*: Liveley, C. M. (1992) 'Parthenogenisis in a freshwater snail: reproductive assurance versus parasitic release', *Evolution*, **46**, (4), Society for the Study of Evolution; *Figure 2.3*: Martyn F. Chillmaid/Science Photo Library; *Figure 2.4*: Wickler, W. (1968) *Mimicry in plants and animals*, Chapter 13, Orion Publishing Group Limited; *Figure 2.5*: Merijn Salverda; *Figure 2.6*: Welch, V. L. *et al.* (2001) *Ecological Entomology*, **26**, Blackwell Publishers Limited; *Figure 2.7*: Courtesy of American Lyme Disease Foundation; *Figure 3.1*: Jamoudi, A. and Sachs, J. D. (1999) 'The changing global distribution of malaria: a review', *CID Working Paper*, No. 2. Copyright Harvard University; *Figure 3.2*: Mims *et al.*, *Medical Microbiology*, 2nd edn. Copyright © 1998 Mosby International Limited; *Figure 3.3*: Peter Barker/Panos; *Figure 3.5*: WHO/TDR/Stammers; *Figures 3.8 and 3.9*: Anderson, R. M. and May, R. M. (1991) 'Microparasites', *Infectious Diseases of Humans*, from Registrar-General's weekly infectious disease return for England and Wales. Crown copyright material is reproduced under Class Licence Number Co1W0000065 with the permission of the Controller of HMSO and the Queen's Printer for Scotland; *Figure 3.8*: Alan Carey/Science Photo Library; *Figure 3.10*: Courtesy of Lacy Hyche, Associate Professor, Department of Entomology and Plant Pathology, Auburn University; *Figure 3.14:* Adapted from Stevens, J. R. *et al.* (1999) 'The ancient and divergent origins of the human pathogenic trypanosomes, *Trypanosoma brucei* and *T. cruzi*', *Parasitology*, **118**, pp.107–116; *Figure 3.15a*: Eye of Science/Science Photo Library; *Figure 3.15b*: Sinclair Stammers/Science Photo Library; *Figure 3.15c*: Courtesy of Rolf Mannesmann, Bielefeld University, Germany; *Figure 3.15d*: Sue Ford/Science Photo Library.

INDEX

Note: Entries in **bold** are key terms. Page numbers referring to information that is given only in a figure or caption are printed in *italics*.